Gratitude

Last but far from least is my husband and life partner, Brady Miller. He has been with me, supporting the long hours of cramming and stress throughout my educational process, my dietetic internships in the medical center, my role as director of integrative medicine at a physician's practice and ultimately as my greatest supporter in the opening of Naturally Nourished. Brady is patient with my new recipes and gracefully eats those that flop, while providing feedback where improvement is needed. His input has been critical for the development of dishes that please the masses and keep you coming back for seconds. Brady is patient and kind and he believes in me. He helps me to see things that I didn't even know were possible and is ultimately my best friend, helping me find light in even the most daunting, overwhelming moments. Brady believes in my mission and my passion and provides a support system to make it all a reality.

Current Medical Model:
Over-medicate, Cover the Symptom, Deal with it!

Growing up in a household with a nurse as a mother, I was always interested in caring for others and working to heal them. I recall all too often being the little tomboy in the neighborhood

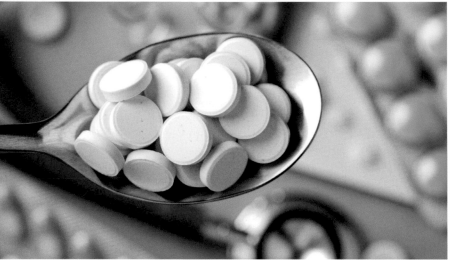

sticking Neosporin and colored Band-Aids on my friends' proudly earned scrapes and scratches.

If I had known then what I know now about the influence of antibacterial compounds not being very effective, I would have used raw unfiltered honey mixed with turmeric, a mixture that is anti-microbial, anti-viral, anti-bacterial and anti-inflammatory; ultimately aiding in reducing the risk of infection and healing the wound!

Early in my adult journey of education and exploration in the medical field, I quickly learned about the blanket treatments being given to patients; how many of them were unnecessary, and how many of them yielded undesired outcomes. I was further disheartened to learn about the many doctors who refuse to acknowledge side effects from drugs when reported from patients; offering a "just deal with it" kind of mentality with some even going as far as threatening to fire patients if they stopped taking the medications - without even offering alternative options! I watched intelligent and successful individuals simply give up like cattle going to slaughter, bowing their heads in acceptance of their diagnosis or state of disease.

I have experienced other people continuing to feel unwell, popping their over the counter Tums, Advil, Excedrin, Gas-x and coping with symptoms; simply surviving rather than thriving, taking their pain and discomfort as just the way their body functions. What if I told you that your body is an adaptable, powerful machine and that it can recover from dysfunction? It can become rebalanced; it can digest optimally, it can rebuild neurotransmitters for brain and mood health, it can regenerate and recover and it can fight against tumors!

This book is an application-oriented guide to learn how to nourish and heal yourself. The following pages will explain the concept of food-as-medicine and how you can successfully use it daily to support your body from the foundation, addressing the root causes of chronic conditions.

What is food-as-medicine?

Food-as-medicine is the understanding that food can serve as a contributor to disease and dysfunction or as a driver for optimal organ function and disease treatment or prevention. By avoiding inflammatory, processed, toxic ingredients and food-like-substances through a whole foods based diet, one is using food as medicine. However, they can take it further by enhancing

NATURALLY
Nourished
FOOD-AS-MEDICINE FOR OPTIMAL HEALTH

BY:
ALI MILLER, RD, LD, CDE

Naturally Nourished LLC

ISBN: 978-0692579312

First Edition, Second Printing

Text by Ali Miller, RD, LD, CDE

Supplemental Text by: Carli Vogler, RD, LD

Photography by: Becki O'Brien

Edited by: Jodie Eisenhardt

www.AliMillerRD.com

Printed in China

TABLE OF CONTENTS

Introduction

Gratitude...1
What is food-as-medicine?....................................3
What is a therapeutic food?..................................5
The role of your digestive health in wellness..........6
Understanding Metabolism...................................8
How clean eating fuels your body's function?.......10
How to navigate this book?................................11

Recipes

Smoothies..13
Breakfasts..35
Salads..59
Soups..83
Snacks...99
Entrees...119
Seafood Entrees...121
Red Meat Entrees..131
Poultry Entrees...147
Veggie Sides...161
Indulgences...179
Therapeutic Foods..209
Dressings and Sauces..225
Food Sensitivity Index..245

Appendix

12 Week meal plans...249

Glossary of Terms & Resources

Resources...273

Gratitude

Creating this book has been a vision in the making for many years and I am absolutely thrilled that it has finally manifested and made its way into your hands! It has been quite the process of recipe development, nutrition research, and organization to ensure this product would be one that you use as a daily resource; for recipes that nourish and as a source of information, inspiring you to eat whole, non-processed foods that heal! I could never have done this on my own and am grateful for those who've played a role in bringing it to fruition. I have quite the dream team of staff at my private practice, Naturally Nourished, and all have played a role in making it happen, but there are a couple of people that deserve a specific shout-out for their significant role in this project.

Carli Vogler, RD, LD is my vice president and serves as my right-side woman. She has been with Naturally Nourished from the first 6 months of opening, and serves as an amazing sound board that keeps my crazy innovator ideas on track, while honing in on the vision projects to make them a reality. She is patient with my sometimes unrealistic expectations and deadlines and always grinds along with me to make things happen. She, too is passionate about the mission of food-as-medicine and gives her all to ensure the philosophy is spread to the masses. Going on her third year with the company, Carli has also grown into a skilled functional medicine practitioner, aiding in the growth on the clinical side as well as business and media aspects. She played a role in developing the concept and flow of this book through many long "think tank" meetings with me, and she worked to assess all of the food-as-medicine information to ensure the unique content and diversity within the 12-week matrices in the appendix.

A great cookbook is only as good as the photos that tell the story of the dishes. Becki O'Brien is our food photographer and nutrition therapist at Naturally Nourished. She works with our blog at www.AliMillerRD.com and has taken all of the beautiful images you'll see in this book. Becki's passion for nutrition and natural foods has been a great asset in the development of this book, as she was able to play a significant role in editing recipes through their reproduction for photography, providing much needed feedback in recipe development. Becki's artistic eye and skills have allowed these recipes to jump off the page and make your mouth water. Without these photographs, the book would not have its strength of reaching the reader on the level of desire. Real food and nourishing food can be indulgent, delicious, and can also satisfy cravings. Becki's photos help to tell this story and inspire you to become excited about eating clean!

their diet with food-as-medicine through the addition of therapeutic ingredients that promote healthy function in the body and lead to optimal metabolic balance. With the use of food-as medicine, you can gain a multitude of treatments for a single intention without undesired side effects from a mono-focused medication.

As an example, using beans to lower cholesterol at ¾ cup per day can decrease your LDL levels by 8% in a 3-month period, as seen in a meta-analysis research study by the Journal of American College of Nutrition in 2007. While doing this, you are also providing your body with fiber to aid in satiety, slowing the breakdown of carbohydrates into sugar, and aiding in the detoxification of the body. In addition to fiber, legumes provide therapeutic nutrients such as magnesium, folate, and B-vitamins to promote blood vessel health, balanced stress response, and reduced homocysteine levels. This synergistic impact of food-as-medicine provides support for the whole system rather than looking to isolate one biomarker of cholesterol. We can see more cardiovascular support with food-as-medicine interventions on lab values such as homocysteine, an independent risk factor for heart and vessel disease. Homocysteine is also reduced with increased bean intake while also reducing blood sugar and blood pressure, which are drivers of vascular injury. Also, the function of lowering cholesterol from legumes works with the system to sequester or trap the excess cholesterol in the body rather than blocking an essential metabolic pathway as most pharmaceutical drugs do.

The most common drug treatment for cholesterol levels is a statin medication. These drugs block an enzyme in the body called HMG CoA Reductase. Along the biological production pathway of this enzyme is cholesterol, the targeted steroid hormone, but there are also many other key players in your body's optimal functionality that are made in this pathway - and they, too are blocked by a statin drug. This pathway of formation or use of cholesterol as a steroid hormone builder plays a role in the production of vitamin D, serotonin, testosterone, and the enzyme CoQ10. So now as your cholesterol levels decline with use of a statin drug, your physician taps you on the shoulder to say good job on your lowered cholesterol levels while you arrive deficient in vitamin D, depressed and anxious from low serotonin, feeling depleted with low libido or erectile dysfunction from declining testosterone, weaker from muscle breakdown, and presenting at higher risk for Alzheimer's' disease and Diabetes. This sets us up for a potential cocktail of medications to cover up the deficiencies of the statin drug and then each of those newly prescribed drugs also have their own list of side effects, thus creating the vicious cycle of the "pharmageddon"!

All too often a medication is prescribed for a condition that can be corrected by repleting a micronutrient deficiency. If using food-as-medicine, you can correct the targeted symptom or condition, facilitating favorable outcomes with varied conditions while correcting the driving cause, versus covering it up. At Naturally Nourished, we see clinical trends when running micronutrient panels on patients. For instance, a patient with depression, fatigue, thinning hair, and diabetes can see positive clinical outcomes with the identification and repletion of biotin deficiency since biotin plays a role in mood stability, along with the utilization of glucose as fuel, the production of amino acids for hair growth, and the release of insulin from the pancreas to aid in blood sugar regulation. All of these favorable outcomes can come from repleting micronutrient deficiency and that same client may also receive the added benefit of reduced blood pressure as biotin aids in relaxing smooth muscles. Rather than leading to undesired side effects and causing a chain reaction of more medication need, food-as-medicine can address the symptoms and conditions from the root cause while providing a multitude of beneficial outcomes.

What is a therapeutic food?

A therapeutic food is an ingredient that yields health outcomes beyond calories, carbs, protein, and fat. Therapeutic foods can provide beneficial outcomes on digestion by fueling bile flow or enzyme production, balancing gut bacteria, or maintaining healthy motility. Therapeutic foods can provide autoimmune support by healing the gut lining and reducing inflammatory responses in the body, providing micronutrient and antioxidant support to reduce excessive immune response, and reducing inflammatory compounds that drive autoimmune expression. Beyond digestive and autoimmune dysfunction, there are therapeutic foods that can influence every ailment and disease condition from diabetes to cardiovascular disease, hormonal imbalance and beyond!

This book is dedicated to the mission that good health starts with real food and real food starts in your kitchen! The recipes have been carefully selected to feature therapeutic ingredients that can correct micronutrient deficiency, balance blood sugar levels, reduce inflammation, and support optimal metabolism and organ function. I have worked to include a strategic combination of ingredients to sing on the palate while synergistically providing food-as-medicine support for your system. Not only will you learn how to make recipes that will make you come back for more, but you will learn about each recipe's superfood ingredient to empower you in learning how food can heal your body.

I have geared my career as a functional medicine practitioner to use food-as-medicine as the foundation of treatment plans and pride myself on nutritional research and an extensive knowledge base that will expand your horizons beyond "because it's good for you". I feel strongly that if you can understand how these foods work in your body, you will learn to redefine your relationship with food and learn to desire and crave whole, real foods in their most natural form.

The Role of your Digestive Health in Wellness

Food allergies and sensitivities are on the rise in America. In fact, according to a study released in 2013 by the Centers for Disease Control and Prevention, food allergies among children increased approximately 50% between 1997 and 2011.

The health impact of food allergies and sensitivities can range from immediate hypersensitivity, such as hives and shortness of breath as seen with allergies, to delayed inflammatory response, seen as sensitivities. These sensitivities can be identified as the cause of IBS, weight gain, bloating, migraines, ADHD, autoimmune disease, and other inflammatory disorders. When our immune system is triggered by a food, it responds with inflammation. The body can also have autoimmune reactions or can attack itself when attempting to attack this "foreign invader". As these reactions continue to present with increasing incident in Americans, it is important to examine why food allergies are on the rise and understand the culprits that contribute to their development. It is interesting to consider how food reactions seem to pop up out of nowhere. How can someone all-of-a-sudden have a reaction to avocados, for example, when they had been eating them for a long time? And why does the body decide to attack certain foods?

Why are food allergies/sensitivities on the rise?

Greater than 80% of our immune system is regulated by our gut. We are beginning to realize the significance of the positive-acting bacteria and probiotics living in our gut and their ability to break down food, inhibit cancer growth, aid in the absorption of nutrients, and work to maintain a healthy gut lining. The intestinal lining is very important, as this is the area where our food is absorbed through the gut-blood barrier. If our intestines are damaged through medications, tap water, gluten, exposure to toxins/food irritants, etc., we will be leaking large food proteins into the bloodstream. This "leaky gut" can allow too large of food particles to pass, setting off alarms (inflammatory compounds) in our immune system in reaction to these proteins that are now seen as "foreign invaders". Once the inflammatory response from a specific food allergen is detected, the body will continue to flag it as an invader. The rise in the use of antibacterial products, oral antibiotics, and vaccines has decreased our exposure to bacteria and viruses, which weakens our immune system, while the excessive sterility can kill off the probiotic colonies.

How our food system influences the rise in gut dysfunction

Beyond the role of bacteria, the way food is produced in our industrialized system impacts the prevalence of gut dysfunction, primarily due to hybrid grains yielding higher amounts of gluten and genetically modified (GMO) crops. GMOs are made from inserting a gene from an external organism to another species to yield desired outcomes; however, the outcomes typically backfire beyond intended effects. Bt corn, is a genetically modified crop containing Bacillus thuringiensis (Bt), a biological pesticide. Bt works as an endotoxin, literally exploding the gut of the caterpillar consuming the crop so it can no longer consume food, nor reproduce, and eventually die. These effects can be seen with intestinal enteropathy, "leaky gut", in the consumers of these crops and their products such as non-organic corn in the form of cornstarch, corn chips, high fructose corn syrup, and more! Beyond direct effects to humans, we can see magnified inflammatory effects in the consumption of the animal products that consume this GMO grain, which is why we strongly advocate for grass-fed, pasture-raised, antibiotic and hormone-free proteins. In addition to gluten and GMOs; processed ingredients, excessive sugars, and synthetic additives in our food system cause our body to have to filter out more gunk than the ability to absorb nutrients, which can stress the digestive tract causing irritation, reactivity, and inflammation.

How this book heals your gut

All the recipes in this book are gluten-free to avoid the abrasive irritating effects of the gliadin protein found in gluten on the GI tract. The book is also low-allergen, focused on avoidance of typical gut irritants and listing other common sources of allergens such as egg, dairy, and grains. By focusing on a whole foods diet using single ingredients, you are more easily able to identify potential dietary irritants while allowing your gut to reset and reduce the inflammatory response.

In the therapeutic section of this book, you will find recipes such as bone broth and gelatin to support gut integrity or repair the process of leaky gut. Bone broth is a traditional food made from the carcass of a roasted chicken or the marrow bone or knuckle bones of beef. Following our bone broth recipe will ensure you are able to leach all the minerals and vital compounds from the ingredients including collagen, gelatin, and L-glutamine - all play a role in the tightening and sealing of the GI junctions. Bone broth is used in many of our nourishing recipes as a base or liquid.

Understanding Metabolism

Metabolism...this word is tossed around commonly in the wellness and weight loss worlds. We know we want to "boost" it but what is it and how does our metabolism impact our body?

In medical terms, metabolism is defined as the set of life-sustaining biochemical transformations and reactions within the cells of every living organism. These metabolic functions allow us to grow and reproduce, maintain cellular structural function, digest and absorb nutrients, and respond to our environment. In the world of metabolism, we are either building through anabolism or breaking down through catabolism. In an anabolic state, we are able to build muscle, repair tissue, and provide our nucleotides for production of DNA - the very code of our being (kind of a big deal).

In a catabolic state, we are able to partake in cellular respiration, the process in the body where we turn nutrients into energy or burn excess calories from our stores to yield weight loss.

The use of fat storage as fuel in weight loss is the primary focus for many people, but before I go into how to optimize this process, it is important to understand that whole body metabolic function is the catalyst of our wellness.

Beyond managing our ability to maintain a healthy weight and burn calories, metabolism plays a role in ensuring the body is able to function optimally, in a state free of disease. In an ideal setting, we have all the nutrients available in our system necessary to build everything the body needs for balanced function. Also, in an ideal setting our metabolic pathways are able to tag environmental toxins, medication by-products, and food additives as foreign invaders and adequately excrete them out of our system.

But what happens when the balance of nutrients to toxins is tipped out of our favor?

When the body is overwhelmed with excess load on metabolic detoxification pathways and not supported with adequate nutrition to fuel them, we get toxins stuffed into storage packages in the form of excessive body fat stores. Interesting to consider; we are now discovering in medical research that our fat cells are functioning as endocrine (hormonal) cells. This interferes with our metabolic pathways, causing irregular elevated blood sugar, decreased caloric burning activity, and the promotion of additional fat storage, verses burn. This creates a vicious cycle creating more fat storage and weight gain.

What happens when we restrict calories to promote catabolism for weight loss but we are lacking the nutrients necessary to fuel the pathways of energy production?

If we just restrict our calories to promote weight loss and do not provide the necessary nutrients for energy production, the body will auto-metabolize from the muscle rather than the fat stores. This is where weight loss and desired body composition change is beyond calorie restriction, as in the case of restriction with inadequate nourishment: The body knows it needs nutrients that it does not get from metabolizing its fat stores, so it goes into muscle breakdown. This is concerning, as our metabolic rate or caloric burn is based on pounds of lean body mass and vital organ functioning.

If you were burning at a baseline of 1600 calories and wanted to lose one pound a week, you may reduce your calories to 1100 (note: it requires a deficit of 500 calories a day to burn one pound at 3,500 calories). If you don't ensure nutritional balance and you aren't fueling your muscle with adequate protein, you will still lose the weight but at the end of 3 months, 12 pounds less, you may be at a reduced metabolic rate of 1100 calories, as you lost your metabolically active muscle mass. This is where you reach a plateau, get frustrated, and fall off! For optimal metabolism and sustainable weight loss, you need a balance of all required nutrients in addition to adequate fat and protein in order to promote optimal metabolic function.

The recipes in this book are specifically formulated to do just this. All recipes are low-glycemic, pairing healthy fats and adequate protein with fibrous carbohydrates to provide support to lean mass while encouraging loss from body fat stores.

Taking it a step further, all dishes are complemented with therapeutic foods to provide an abundance of micronutrients and antioxidants that reduce inflammation, balance blood sugar levels, and boost metabolic burn.

How clean eating
fuels your body's function

When using food-as-medicine in treatment plans for complementary alternative care, it is important to have a potent food source. Industrialized farming methods have stripped our produce of vitamins, minerals, and antioxidants, while creating toxicity with insecticides, pesticides, herbicides, and fungicides. I feel with a strong sense of urgency the need to educate and connect people to their local food system. A primary way to ensure a high integrity of food is to decentralize our food system. We need to redistribute farm subsidies from commercially grown crops (genetically modified corn and soy, industrialized wheat, cotton, and canola) to sustainably grown foods grown on a smaller scale with thriving soil and biodiversity of heirloom varietals. Eating clean and selecting the most nourishing ingredients will ensure you are optimizing your metabolism with an abundance of antioxidants and therapeutic nutrients while avoiding the negative influence of toxins burdening metabolism and driving fat storage.

Choose nourishing ingredients to get the most value out of the recipes

The best way you can ensure nourishing clean options is through eating locally and seasonally. The recipes in this book are focused on simple, nourishing ingredients that highlight seasonal produce and whole food ingredients. All recipes are free of flour and refined grain products as well as refined processed sugars and artificial ingredients, as these foods are void of nutrients and taxing on our metabolic processes. Produce selections should be organic, local or sustainably grown wherever possible to ensure the most nutritional density.

It is with intention and purpose that ingredients selected are full fat and non-processed. Dairy should be non-homogenized and low-heat processed or raw and from grass-fed sources if possible to retain the delicate nutrients such as immunoglobulins, antioxidants, and conjugated linoleic acids (CLA) which boost immune health and metabolism. These nutrients reduce with excessive heat processing and are increased with grass-fed or pasture-raised products. This is also important when selecting your proteins. Red meat and poultry should be grass-fed or pasture-raised and fish should be wild-caught to ensure more omega-3 fatty acids, more minerals, and to ensure a less toxic inflammatory product. Conventional meats are often fed genetically modified feed and injected with synthetic growth hormones and antibiotics which will bioaccumulate in their flesh and wreck havoc on our gut and metabolic processes.

How to navigate this book

What is Balanced Eating for a Diet-free Lifestyle?

Over-restriction is the precursor to over-indulgence! Let's face it, we all have an emotional relationship with food, but just like any relationship, some are supportive and some are imbalanced or taxing. For thousands of years, food has played an integral role in ceremony, celebration, and of course, survival. There are very innate needs or desires that can be met with nutrient-dense whole foods providing nourishment for your body along with building blocks for a sound mind, while also reducing toxicity or imbalance in the system.

For instance, humans tend to crave or desire sweet foods over those which are bitter, which is a great part of why we are here today. Many bitter, astringent plants are toxic and in the hunter and gatherer days, harvesting bitter foods may have been the last meal experienced followed by a painful death from toxic overload. Also, upon birth the first production of breast milk is made up of colostrum; a nutrient-dense, probiotic-rich, high fat concentrated delivery of nourishment to provide infants with optimal growth and development. Colostrum also happens to be sweet and so immediately from birth, the palate is drawn towards this taste.

Unfortunately, the food industry has taken this "sweet tooth" to the extreme, refining sugars until they are void of nutrients and concentrating them to pack in an excessive amount of sugar, greatly altering our taste buds in the process to expect these artificially induced flavors. From non-caloric, chemically derived sweeteners that drive us into insulin resistance with undesired impacts on neurological health, to high fructose corn syrup, we can no longer trust our taste buds to lead us to nourishment or to foods that are safe. Nonetheless, we need to work with our body to better understand our cravings and the role that our food selections play in our body, both physically and psychologically.

This book includes an indulgences section that provides nourishing options that fuel your body's function while satisfying cravings. I believe in satisfying sugar cravings while teaching the body to channel savory and enjoy complex flavors such as acids, tannins, and varied textures. I do not

support the use of stevia or other natural non-caloric sweeteners as they set us up for unrealistic sweet tastes and create insulin resistance in the body where the tongue tastes sweet and sends a physiological cascade of reactions producing insulin, a pro-inflammatory hormone that is focused to move glucose out of the bloodstream and into your body's cells.

However, when there is no glucose present with the consumption of non-caloric and non-carbohydrate sweeteners, we get a release of insulin which leads to insulin resistance. In this scenario, the cells become desensitized to the insulin due to the lack of function in this phantom blood sugar response. I have consciously selected nourishing sweeteners to use in these recipes which come from sources that provide your body with vitamins, minerals, and nutrients while taming sugar cravings and allowing for a natural physiological blood sugar response.

How to navigate this book

This book is broken into sections seen in a typical cookbook to aid in navigation of the types of recipes that you desire to make. If you are new to clean eating and looking for a plan, I recommend using the 12-week meal plan matrixes in the back of the book. These feature 2 breakfast options, 3 entrees, and 4 unique snacks per week in a 1200 and 1800 calorie breakdown geared towards weight loss for both women and men or based on your particular calorie range from your activity factor of exercise.

When making the recipes and reading ingredients, refer to the Resources section in the back of the book for information and tips on sourcing and using ingredients you may be unfamiliar with. This section also provides qualitative information to distinguish good-better-best when selecting your food choices, ensuring you are able to get successful outcomes with the recipes while utilizing the most nourishing products.

I encourage you to be mindful of the food-as-medicine facts in each recipe as they will create connection on why the ingredients carefully selected matter and inspire you to use these in your weekly meal plans beyond the recipes provided.

Work through the book by section or navigate with a weekly matrix to explore food-as-medicine and begin to heal your body from the inside out. You will find that in addition to improved energy, reduced pain, improved cognitive function, and blood sugar balance that weight loss is often a pleasant side-effect!

Smoothies

Berry Yogurt Smoothie
Cool It Down Smoothie
PSL Redo
Cacao Coffee Boost
Pear Basil Cucumber Smoothie
Superfood Smoothie
Minty Cacao Green Smoothie
Peachy Keen Smoothie
Tropical Bliss Smoothie

How to Build a Balanced Smoothie:

1) Be sure to include healthy fats!
These create a balanced blood sugar response by blunting the glycemic spike of the blended fruits. Fats also promote satiety or feeling of fullness while nourishing the brain and nervous system. Choose from: chia, hemp, flax seeds, nut butter, nuts, coconut shreds, coconut oil, coconut milk, organic whole fat milk, or avocado.

2) Watch the fruit intake!
Aim for low-glycemic options and stay within max 1 cup! Select organic frozen or add ice if desired, choose from: berries, ⅓ banana, tropical fruits (mango, pineapple), stone fruit (peaches, plumbs) and others for variety. Limit 2-3 choices max to ensure your flavors don't get mucky!

3) Include 1-2 Food-as-Medicine boosts from roots, herbs, and spices!
These add antioxidants, minerals, vitamins and other disease fighting compounds while boosting the flavor! Choose from: fresh herbs, ginger, turmeric root, cinnamon, maca, matcha powder, and more!

4) If using as a meal, be sure to add a protein!
Grass-fed Whey is best, if tolerated; look for non-denatured products for active immune boosting compounds and antioxidants. If a non-dairy option is desired, try a pea protein. Consider adding unsweetened Greek yogurt for a tangy probiotic protein-rich kick!

BERRY YOGURT
SMOOTHIE

BERRY YOGURT SMOOTHIE

Makes:
1 Serving

Ingredients:
1 cup blueberries, frozen
6 oz full fat Greek yogurt
1 tsp vanilla extract
4 oz almond milk, unsweetened
1 Tbsp ground flax seed
1 tsp raw, unfiltered honey

Directions:
Place all ingredients in blender and mix well until creamy.

Nutrition Per Serving:
Calories 297, Total Fat 9g, Carbs 41g, Protein 17g

Food as Medicine Tip:
Blueberries are literally bursting with nutrients and flavor! The added bonus, they are very low in calories. Packed with antioxidant phytonutrients called anthocyanidins, blueberries neutralize free radical damage that can lead to cataracts, glaucoma, varicose veins, hemorrhoids, peptic ulcers, heart disease, and cancer.

COOL IT DOWN
SMOOTHIE

COOL IT DOWN SMOOTHIE

Makes:
2 Servings

Ingredients:
¾ cup water
½ cup pineapple
1 cup cucumber, roughly chopped
⅓ cup full fat, canned coconut milk
10 mint leaves
1-inch ginger root, peeled
1-2 tsp turmeric powder or 1-inch fresh root, peeled
½ cup ice
1 scoop *Naturally Nourished Grass-fed Whey Protein*
Optional: 2 tsp raw, unfiltered honey

Directions:
Blend all ingredients except for the whey. When smooth and creamy, add the whey and blend in tor 5 seconds more, being careful to avoid over-blending and the creation of foam.
Optional: sweeten with raw, unfiltered honey.

Nutrition Per Serving (w/o honey):
Calories 178, Total Fat 9g, Carbs 10g, Protein 13g

Food As Medicine Tip:
This zingy bold focused smoothie packs a punch of antioxidants paired with tropical enzymes to reduce inflammation and cool down the body. The cucumber contributes cooling fibers that contribute to healthy collagen formation in the skin. Coconut milk provides healthy fat to balance the carbs from the pineapple. This smoothie has properties to soothe the GI tract, fight against cancer, reduce joint pain, and boost metabolism!

PSL REDO

PSL REDO

Makes:
1 Serving

Ingredients:
½ cup pumpkin puree
⅓ cup full fat, canned coconut milk
4 oz filtered water
1 pitted date
6 oz cold brewed coffee
¼ tsp ginger
½ tsp cinnamon
pinch of ground cloves
1 scoop *Naturally Nourished Grass-fed Whey Protein*

Directions:
Blend all ingredients except for the whey. When smooth and creamy, add the whey and blend in for 5 seconds more, being careful to prevent over-blending to create foam.

Nutrition Per Serving:
Calories 261, Total Fat 16g, Carbs 20g, Protein 27g

Food as Medicine Tip:
Love the Pumpkin Spice Latte but looking to save on calories and toxins? Indulge in real pumpkin which is a rich source of vitamin A, zinc, and phytocompounds to boost immune function and metabolism with this smoothie while avoiding ingredients found in the typical coffee shop counterpoint, such as potassium sorbate, high fructose corn syrup, caramel coloring, and artificial flavors.

CACAO COFFEE
BOOST

CACAO COFFEE BOOST

Makes:
1 Serving

Ingredients:
1 Tbsp almond butter
6 oz cold brew coffee
2-4 oz water
1 Tbsp cacao powder
2 dates, pitted
1 scoop *Naturally Nourished Grass-fed Whey Protein*

Directions:
Blend all ingredients except for the whey. When smooth and creamy, add the whey and blend in for 5 seconds more, being careful to avoid over-blending and the creation of foam.

Nutrition Per Serving:
Calories 280, Total Fat 12g, Carbs 20g, Protein 24g

Food as Medicine Tip:
This is a perfect post-workout smoothie; just looking forward to having it is motivating! The blend of cacao with almond butter and rich cold brewed coffee makes for a delicious iced mocha and the protein addition makes this indulgence a guilt-free, balanced meal with amino acids to rebuild muscle and boost metabolism!

PEAR BASIL
SMOOTHIE

PEAR BASIL SMOOTHIE

Makes:
1 Serving

Ingredients:
1 medium pear
4 leaves basil
1 cup cucumber, roughly chopped
2 oz full fat, canned coconut milk
1 Tbsp chia seeds
8 oz filtered water (as needed, the cucumber will provide some of the liquid!)
1 scoop *Naturally Nourished Grass-fed Whey Protein*

Directions:
Blend the first six ingredients: pear through water, in the blender until incorporated. Whip in the whey protein at the end and blend until combined, but not overmixed.

Nutrition Per Serving:
Calories 371, Total Fat 19g, Carbs 29g, Protein 29

Food as Medicine Tip:
Cucumbers are incredibly hydrating, and staying adequately hydrated during the hotter months, is crucial. Cucumbers have diuretic properties, which act to flush toxins out of the body and maintain healthy tissue and skin. With significant amounts of vitamin B, phosphorus, calcium, zinc and other minerals, cucumbers aid in balancing electrolytes and boosting metabolism. This smoothie pairs the unique properties of cucumber with aromatic basil and the healthy fat of coconut oil while providing sustained energy and soluble fiber from chia seeds to maintain satiety.

SUPERFOOD
SMOOTHIE

SUPERFOOD SMOOTHIE

Makes:
2 Servings

Ingredients:
1 cup filtered water
1 tsp raw, unfiltered honey
¼ cup full fat, canned coconut milk
Pinch of sea salt
⅛ cup organic Brazil nuts
5 leaves basil
5 leaves mint
1 small apple, cored and sliced
1 tsp maca root powder
2 cups greens (rainbow chard, spinach, kale)
1 scoop *Naturally Nourished Grass-fed Whey Protein*

Directions:
Add water, honey, coconut milk, salt, and Brazil nuts and blend until smooth. These act as your smoothie base. Then add basil, mint, apple slices, maca and blend well. Finally, add greens to further boost nutrient intake. When smooth, add the whey and blend in for 5 seconds more, being careful to avoid over-blending and the creation of foam.

Nutrition Per Serving:
Calories 260, Total Fat 10g, Carbs 28g, Protein 14g

Food as Medicine Tip:
Smoothies are a quick and easy way to pack nutrient density into your day and ensure an easy absorption of health supporting compounds. Switch up your superfoods and always ensure to add a protein and healthy fat for a balanced blended beverage. Blending greens is a great way to increase digestibility and optimal absorption of nutrients.

MINTY CACAO
GREEN SMOOTHIE

MINTY CACAO
GREEN SMOOTHIE

Makes:
1 Serving

Ingredients:
2 oz full fat coconut milk
4 oz filtered water
¼ avocado
1 pitted date
2 cups fresh spinach
3-4 sprigs fresh mint
1 Tbsp raw cacao nibs
1 scoop *Naturally Nourished Grass-fed Whey Protein*

Directions:
Blend the ingredients, coconut milk through mint, in the blender until smooth and creamy. You can add more mint leaves to taste at this point. Add the cacao nibs and whey, blend an additional 10-15 seconds, just until incorporated. The cacao nibs will act as the chocoalte "chips", adding a bit of texture to your smoothie. If you prefer a less textured smoothie, just blend 30 seconds longer, but wait to add the whey to the end so you don't end up with a frothy smoothie! Optional: top with 1 tsp cocoa nibs.

Nutrition Per Serving:
369 Calories, Total Fat 23g, Carbs 27g, Protein 29g

Food as Medicine Tip:
Avocados have a healthy fatty acid profile that has demonstrated through research to protect against prostate and breast cancer as well as heart disease and additionally helps to maintain supple skin. Cacao is the natural bean that chocolate is made from, the nib is the least processed whole food form. Cacao has a high antioxidant capacity exceeding red wine, green tea, and other exotic super foods. Cacao is very high in magnesium, which can help to lower blood pressure levels and relax muscles. Mint is very calming and soothing to the digestive tract and also has a very high antioxidant capacity.

PEACHY KEEN
SMOOTHIE

PEACHY KEEN SMOOTHIE

Makes:
2 Servings

Ingredients:
1 cup filtered water
⅛ cup Brazil nuts
1 Tbsp chia seeds
½ frozen banana
1 cup peaches (fresh or frozen)
2-4 large kale leaves, de-stemmed and roughly chopped
4-5 ice cubes
1 scoop *Naturally Nourished Grass-fed Whey Protein*

Directions:
Combine the water, nuts, and seeds in blender and whip on high to create a nut milk. Add fruit, greens and blend again until smooth. Finally blend in ice and add water if needed to achieve desired consistency. Once smoothie is at the desired texture and flavor, whip in whey for 3-5 seconds to briefly combine, avoiding over-mixing or creating an airy foam.

Nutrition Per Serving:
Calories 249, Total Fat 9g, Carbs 26g, Protein 20g

Food as Medicine Tip:
Peaches can help improve your skin! Peaches are a great source of vitamins A and C. Vitamin A provides moisture to the skin, which improves the skin's texture making it soft and supple. Vitamin C is a powerful antioxidant that protects the skin from free radical damage. Besides eating peaches, as a natural beauty regime, you can also rub peaches directly on your skin to help get rid of dark circles and wrinkles.

TROPICAL BLISS
SMOOTHIE

TROPICAL BLISS SMOOTHIE

Makes:
2 Servings

Ingredients:
⅓ of a frozen banana
¼ mango, peeled
½-inch fresh ginger, peeled
¼ cup full fat, canned coconut milk
¼ cup filtered water
1 Tbsp ground flax seeds
¾ cup cultured Greek yogurt (Greek yogurt has at least 15g of protein in a 6oz Serving)
2 cups greens (spinach, collards, kale, chard, etc)
1 scoop *Naturally Nourished Grass-fed Whey Protein*
Optional: ½ cup of ice

Directions:
Place all ingredients except whey in blender and mix on high until ingredients are blended together and texture is creamy. Add whey after blending and simply incorporate with a spoon or whisk to avoid the creation of a frothy foam.

Nutrition Per Serving:
Calories 351, Total Fat g, Carbs 29g, Protein 26g

Food as Medicine Tip:
This nourishing smoothie has both pre- and pro-biotics to create a symbiotic gut. This refreshing treat is loaded with antioxidants and is anti-inflammatory, helping to cool your body through the effects of the probiotics and the ginger. It is a great healthy snack and a good way to sneak cultured foods, (like Greek yogurt), into your diet!

Breakfasts

Chard Gruyere Frittata
Migas with Spinach and Peppers
Broccoli Cheddar Frittata
Sweet Potato Turkey Sausage and Kale Casserole
Green Eggs and Ham
Plantain Collagen Pancakes
Coco-NOatmeal
Overnight Oatmeal
Blueberry Flaxseed Overnight Oatmeal
Paleo Pumpkin Spice Muffins
Balanced Banana Walnut Muffins

CHARD GRUYERE
FRITTATA

CHARD GRUYERE FRITTATA

Makes:
6 Servings

Ingredients:
10 large eggs
¼ cup grated Parmesan cheese
2 tsp fresh chives, snipped
sea salt and black pepper to taste
⅛ tsp paprika
3 Tbsp butter, separated into 2 Tbsp and 1 Tbsp
2-3 Yukon Gold potatoes; about ½ pound, cut into ½-inch dice (¾ cup)
1 medium onion, thinly sliced
1 bunch chard stems, chopped
2 cloves garlic, minced
1 bunch rainbow chard leaves, chopped
½ cup Gruyere cheese, shredded

Directions:
In a bowl, whisk the eggs, Parmesan cheese, chives, salt, pepper, and paprika. Heat 2 Tbsp butter in 10-inch, cast-iron skillet over medium heat. Add the diced potatoes and cook until tender, about 6-7 minutes. Transfer to a bowl. Add 1 Tbsp more of the butter and sauté the onion, then add stems for additional 1-2 minutes. Then add the garlic and stir continuously to prevent burning. Add the potatoes back to the pan along with another pinch of salt and pepper.

Lower the heat, add the egg mixture to the skillet and stir briefly until distributed, be careful not to over stir or will create a scramble. Add the Gruyere cheese on top. Cook at low heat without stirring for about 10 minutes until the eggs are almost set, the center will still be wet, but small bubbles will appear at the surface. Position the oven rack about 6 inches from the broiler and heat the broiler to medium. Put the skillet under the broiler for about 3-4 min, until eggs are set and top of frittata is golden. Remove from the oven and let set for 5 minutes and then transfer to a plate to cut into wedges. Enjoy!

Optional: If your oven does not have a broiler function, place pan on middle rack of pre-heated oven at 375°F for 10-15 minutes to set and slightly brown. This works well but does not create the caramelized top.

Nutrition Per Serving:
Calories 326, Total Fat 25g, Carbs 8g, Protein 20g

Food as Medicine Tip:
This frittata is a great way to prepare a nutrient-dense breakfast ahead of time to avoid the chaos and stress of the morning. Make this on a Sunday night and have breakfast all week long. Breakfast casseroles, frittatas, and quiches are a great way to incorporate vegetables into your morning meal while ensuring you are meeting your protein needs. In addition to grams of protein, eggs provide a variety of nutrients. Pasture-raised eggs are higher in omega-3s, vitamin E, vitamin D, B-vitamins, and choline, which is a nutrient associated with brain function, maintains vascular health, and hormonal balance.

MIGAS WITH SPINACH
AND PEPPERS

39

MIGAS WITH SPINACH AND PEPPERS

Makes:
6 Servings

Ingredients:
12 large eggs
¼ cup half-and-half
1 Tbsp butter
1 Tbsp olive oil
1 medium onion, chopped
1 yellow bell pepper, roughly chopped
1 red bell pepper, roughly chopped
1 jalapeño, seeds and membranes removed, finely diced
½ cup salsa
2-3 cups crushed baked blue corn organic tortilla chips
1 cup Mexican cheese blend, shredded (may use cotija, cheddar, Monterey Jack, etc.)
1 cup cilantro, chopped
1 package baby spinach
2 cups cooked black beans (or 1 can rinsed black beans)

Directions:
In a bowl, whisk together eggs and half & half, set aside. In a large skillet over medium-high heat, melt the olive oil with the butter. Add onions and bell peppers and cook until starting to brown, about 3-4 minutes. Add in diced jalapeño and stir to combine. Add salsa to the skillet and stir, then add chip pieces, stirring to combine. Reduce heat to low, this is key to ensure you don't overcook your eggs! When the heat has decreased, pour egg mixture into skillet. Stir gently to cook with the peppers, folding mixture as it cooks. Turn off heat, fold in grated cheese and chopped cilantro. Serve on a bed of baby spinach with ⅓-½ cup black beans.

Nutrition Per Serving:
Calories 489, Total Fat 24g, Carbs 45g, Protein 28g

Food as Medicine tip:
The majority of corn used in the United States is a genetically modified version called Bt corn. Bt corn (Bacillus thuringiensis, a biological pesticide), works as an endotoxin, literally exploding the gut of insects that attempt to eat it. When choosing corn products, always purchase the heirloom varieties and organic brands to prevent exposure to these toxins, which can eventually lead to leaky gut!

BROCCOLI CHEDDAR
FRITTATA

BROCCOLI CHEDDAR FRITTATA

Makes:
6 Servings

Ingredients:
10 large eggs
2 Tbsp milk, low-heat, non-homogenized
1 Tbsp butter
1 small red onion, cut in half, then thinly sliced (about ½ cup chopped)
2.5 cups chopped broccoli
¼ tsp salt
Freshly ground pepper to taste
2 ounces extra-sharp cheddar cheese, shredded (½ cup)

Directions:
Preheat the broiler. Combine the eggs and milk in a medium bowl and whisk well. In a medium ovenproof skillet, heat the butter over medium heat. Add the onion and cook, stirring, until it begins to soften, about 3 minutes. Add the broccoli and cook for another 3-4 minutes. Season with salt and pepper. Pour the egg mixture over the vegetables in the skillet, covering them evenly. Do not stir or over agitate or will end up with a scramble instead of a frittata.

Reduce the heat to medium-low, cover, and let cook until the egg mixture has set around the edges of the pan, but is still somewhat liquid in the middle, about 8 minutes. There should be tiny bubbles at the surface. Sprinkle with the cheese and place the skillet under the broiler about 2 inches from the heat until the surface is set and golden brown, 1 to 2 minutes. Be careful not to overcook or the frittata will become tough. Cut the into 8 wedges and serve.

Nutrition Per Serving:
Calories 241, Total Fat 17, Carbs 6g, Protein 16g

Food as Medicine tip:
Eggs are a nutritionally dense food providing choline for brain development, omega-3s for heart health, and a concentration of vitamins, minerals, and antioxidants in a whole food non-processed form. As an animal protein, it is important to consider source and quality as animal products have a biological magnification of toxins and nutrients. Look for pasture-raised eggs or those ranging freely on grasses and grubs. When selecting quality eggs, be sure to consume the yolk as this is where most nutrients are concentrated. Making a frittata is a great way to incorporate vegetables and eggs in a quick reheat throughout the week.

SWEET POTATO AND TURKEY
SAUSAGE KALE
CASSEROLE

SWEET POTATO AND TURKEY SAUSAGE KALE CASSEROLE

Makes:
8 Servings

Ingredients:
1½ Tbsp coconut oil
1 yellow onion, chopped
1 sweet potato, cut into ½-inch cubes (about 1½ cups)
1 Tbsp chili powder
½ tsp sea salt
12 oz 95% lean ground turkey (white meat)
6 oz 85% lean ground turkey (dark meat)
8 whole eggs, whisked
6 egg whites, whisked
1 cup non-homogenized, full fat milk
1 Tbsp sage, choppd
1 bunch curly kale, torn into 1-inch pieces
1 cup shredded Gouda cheese

Directions:
Preheat oven 350°F. Heat cast-iron skillet and melt coconut oil. Sauté onion and sweet pota-to cubes, sprinkle with chili powder and sea salt, sauté for 8-10 minutes until softened. While sweet potato and onion is cooking, in a separate bowl, combine both 95% and 85% turkey until well mixed.

Once sweet potatoes and onion are soft, add ground turkey and heat until cooked through, about 6-8 minutes. While meat is browning, whisk eggs with milk and fresh chopped sage, set aside. Once cooked through (not pink) add in curly kale and stir until coated in juices and beginning to soften, about 1-2 minutes.

Remove from heat and spread veggie and turkey mixture in 12x9-inch casserole pan. Once distributed throughout, pour in egg mixture and press down to ensure all veggies are covered. Top with shredded cheese. Bake in oven covered for first 20 minutes, then uncover and bake an additional 10-15 minutes, until eggs are cooked through and casserole is set in the center. Remove from oven and let cool, about 8-10 minutes, prior to cutting into 8 pieces.

Nutrition Per Serving:
Calories 361, Total Fat 17g, Carbs 20g, Protein 31g

Food As Medicine Tip:
Anthocyanin compounds in sweet potatoes have anti-inflammatory effects and can target brain and blood vessel health. Sweet potatoes can also aid in the release of adiponectin, a hormone in fat cells that work favorably with insulin response to balance blood sugar levels. Sweet potatoes are an excellent source of beta-carotene and will help reduce your risk for cancers. There are over 300 carotenoid compounds and beta-carotene is just one of them! Research supports the synergy of consuming them together in carotene rich food sources as far superior to isolated carotenoids in synthetic supplemental form, which may contribute to higher disease risk.

GREEN EGGS
AND HAM

GREEN EGGS AND HAM

Makes:
3 Servings

Ingredients:
6 large eggs
2.5 cups spinach
4-6 large fresh basil leaves, chopped, plus extra basil chopped for garnish
2 tsp butter
¼ cup Parmesan cheese
sea salt and pepper to taste
6 oz lean ham (nitrate free, organic)
Optional: sautéed veggies, such as peppers, mushrooms, zucchini, squash or broccoli

Directions:
Blend the eggs, spinach and basil together until smooth and green in a blender or food processor. Grease a skillet with a light coating of butter. Pour the mixture into the pan and cook slowly over medium heat. Using a rubber spatula, pull the edges of the eggs toward the middle. Repeat until the eggs are cooked to your liking as a scramble, folding in cheese. Season with salt and pepper, if desired. Using the same skillet, place the ham into one layer. Let brown for about 1 minute and flip. Repeat till all ham is warmed and brown. Serve green eggs with your seared ham, chopped basil and optional added sautéed vegetables!

Nutrition Per Serving (with ham):
Calories 237, Total Fat 16, Carbs 4g, Protein 23g

Food As Medicine Tip:
Don't be fooled by out-of-date recommendations! It has been proven that cholesterol in the diet, including that found in egg yolks does not raise the cholesterol in the blood. In fact, eggs primarily raise the "good" cholesterol and are not associated with heart disease. Pasture-raised eggs from chickens eating grasses are high in all sorts of nutrients including choline, omega-3s, vitamin D, and B-vitamins along with unique antioxidants that protect our eyes.

PLANTAIN COLLAGEN
PANCAKES

PLANTAIN COLLAGEN PANCAKES

Makes:
6 Servings

Ingredients:
2 large green plantains (about 2 cups, pureed)
3 large eggs
2 tsp vanilla
2 tsp cinnamon
3 Tbsp butter
2 Tbsp Collagen powder (Vital Choice Collagen)
¼ tsp sea salt
½ tsp baking soda
2 Tbsp coconut oil for cooking in cast-iron

Directions:
Peel plantains, then add to large bowl with eggs and mix until well incorporated. Once homogenous, add remaining ingredients through baking soda and blend on high for about 2 minutes until the mixture becomes velvety. Heat a cast iron skillet on medium heat and add 2 tsp coconut oil at a time for each pancake. Pour ¼ cup of batter per pancake onto the skillet, maintaining medium heat. Allow pancake to bubble slightly on top surface. After about 4 minutes of cooking, flip to cook for an additional 2 minutes. Remove pancake from pan and wrap in foil while waiting for remaining batter to cook. Continue to add coconut oil to pan to prevent sticking. Serve pancakes with two slices of pasture-raised, nitrite-free bacon, sauteed fruit, or berries and nuts with coconut creme!

Nutrition Per Serving:
Calories 151, Total Fat 10g, Carbs 13g, Protein 4g

Food as Medicine Tip:
Plantains are a great source of potassium and fiber and are considered a "resistant starch." Resistant starch is a type of starch that is not digested in the stomach or small intestine, reaching the colon intact. Thus, it "resists" digestion. When eating resistant starches, we do not see spikes in blood glucose or insulin after and also do not obtain significant calories from eating them. Pro-bacteria feed on resistance starches and produce short chain fatty acids via fermentation, including acetate, butyrate, and propionate, which are beneficial in protection against diseases like colon cancer.

COCO-NOATMEAL

COCO-NOATMEAL

Makes
4 Servings

Ingredients:
1 cup shredded unsweetened coconut
2 Tbsp almond flour
½ cup full fat, canned coconut milk
½ cup filtered water (more as needed to thin)
½ tsp ground cardamom
1 tsp ground cinnamon
½ tsp ground ginger
1 tsp vanilla extract
pinch sea salt
Additional ¼-½ cup filtered water, as needed to thin
2 scoops *Naturally Nourished Grass-fed Whey Protein*
Optional: berries and nuts of your choice
Optional: extra cinnamon and coconut shreds for sprinkling

Directions:
Place the first nine ingredients, coconut through sea salt, in a small saucepan over medium heat. Cook, stirring occasionally until the mixture begins to thicken and coconut starts to soften and absorb the liquid, about 10 minutes. You can add more filtered water as needed to thin out the mixture. Remove from heat and stir in the whey protein powder. Spoon into a bowl and top with berries or nuts. Sprinkle with cinnamon and coconut to top. You can make this ahead of time and store individual Servings for up to three days in mason jars—it only gets better with time!

Nutrition Per Serving:
Calories 262, Total Fat 19g, Carbs 7g, Protein 15g

Food as Medicine Tip:
This grain free "oatmeal" uses shredded coconut instead of oats, making it a great low-carb alternative to traditional oatmeal, that is equally satiating and delicious when you're craving a warm breakfast. Coconut contains medium-chain fatty acids (MCTs,) which work to tonify the adrenal glands, aid in sleep regulation, reduce stress and boost the metabolism. While saturated fat once got a bad rap, we are now learning that eating this type of fat can aid in weight loss and appetite regulation and even be heart protective! Coconut also contains lauric and caprylic acids, which have antibacterial, antifungal and antiviral benefits. Caprylic acid also has the unique ability to combat yeast overgrowth in the body. The addition of grass-fed whey supports lean body mass and cognitive function, making this a balanced breakfast!

OVERNIGHT
OATMEAL

OVERNIGHT OATMEAL

Makes:
1 Serving

Ingredients:
¼ cup dry rolled oats
⅓ cup almond milk (dairy milk, or milk of your choice)
½ cup plain Greek yogurt
½ cup berries (or fruit of your choice)
2 tsp chia seeds
optional: 1 tsp raw, unfiltered honey

Directions:
Add ingredients to container with a lid, stir to mix ingredients. Shake well for at least 30 seconds, then store in refrigerator overnight. You can make this quick recipe up to three days ahead, or make a couple at a time to help make the chaos of breakfast a relaxed quick grab and go!

Nutrition Per Serving:
Calories 252, Total Fat 7g, Carbs 32g, Protein 16g

Food as Medicine Tip:
Aim for a daily source of probiotics! Probiotics are live microbial food ingredients that have a direct and indirect effect on our health. They work directly to regulate our digestive tracts, decrease gas and bloating, defend against food allergies, and increase the ability to absorb nutrients, vitamins, and minerals from our food. Indirectly, probiotics work to improve our immune system, defend against cancer, decrease inflammation, and act as natural antibiotics.

BLUEBERRY FLAXSEED
OVERNIGHT OATMEAL

BLUEBERRY FLAXSEED OVERNIGHT OATMEAL

Makes:
1 Serving

Ingredients:
⅔ cup Greek yogurt, 2% or whole fat
1½ Tbsp flax seed, freshly ground
⅓ cup blueberries
3 Tbsp rolled oats
⅓ cup almond milk
optional: 1-2 tsp raw, unfiltered honey

Directions:
Place ingredients in jar with lid, seal and shake. Place in refrigerator overnight. Make a couple at a time as each jar is good for 3-4 days!

Nutrition Per Serving:
Calories 252, Total Fat 7g, Carbs 32g, Protein 16g

Food as Medicine Tip:
Flax seed is a great source of fiber, omega-3 fatty acids, and lignans. The omega-3 is in the form of Alpha Linolenic Acid (ALA) and the lignans aid in detoxifying excess estrogens in the body, working to fight against estrogen dominance and hormone related cancer. To ensure optimal antioxidants and nutrients, purchase in whole form and grind with coffee grinder or blender and store in a glass, airtight jar in freezer.

PALEO PUMPKIN
SPICE MUFFINS

PALEO PUMPKIN SPICE MUFFINS

Makes:
12 Servings

Ingredients:
½ cup coconut flour
½ cup almond flour
½ tsp baking soda
½ tsp baking powder
1 scoop *Naturally Nourished Grass-fed Whey Protein*
¼ tsp salt
1½ tsp ground cinnamon
½ tsp freshly grated nutmeg
½ tsp ground cloves
2 Tbsp melted butter
2 Tbsp melted coconut oil
⅓ cup sucanat or date sugar
¼ cup grade b maple syrup
3 eggs
1¼ cups pumpkin puree (make sure only ingredient is organic pumpkin, no added sugar)
1 tsp vanilla extract

Directions:
Preheat oven to 350°F and line a standard size muffin tin with unbleached liners. In a medium bowl, combine coconut flour, almond flour, baking soda, baking powder, protein powder, salt, and spices. In a large bowl, whisk together the butter, coconut oil, sucanat, syrup, eggs, pumpkin, and vanilla. Pour the dry ingredients into the wet and stir to combine. Batter will be thick. Portion into your muffin liners. Bake until puffed and cooked through, about 35-40 minutes; check at 30 minutes.

Nutrition Per Serving:
Calories 167, Total Fat 8g, Carbs 18g, Protein 7g

Food as Medicine Tip:
Just one cup of cooked pumpkin offers 200% of your daily needed vitamin A in a form that best protects your vision. The soluble fiber and zinc in pumpkin play a role for blood sugar and insulin regulation while the phytosterols in the seeds aid in lowering your bad cholesterol levels. The abundance of antioxidants serve to scavenge free radicals while protecting against oxidative damage and also decrease inflammation in the body.

BALANCED BANANA
WALNUT MUFFINS

BALANCED BANANA WALNUT MUFFINS

Makes:
12 Servings

Ingredients:
1½ cups hazelnut flour
1½ cups rolled oats, pulsed in food processor to make a flour
1½ scoops *Naturally Nourished Grass-fed Whey Protein*
1 tsp cinnamon
½ tsp sea salt
1½ tsp baking soda
1½ Tbsp butter, melted (or coconut oil)
3 large eggs
4 ripe bananas, mashed
2 tsp vanilla extract
⅛ cup chia seeds

Directions:
Preheat oven to 350°F and line pan with unbleached baking cups. Combine hazelnut flour, oat flour, protein powder, cinnamon, salt and baking soda in large bowl. Whisk together butter, eggs, bananas, and vanilla extract in a medium bowl. Add wet ingredients to the dry and stir to combine. Fold in chia seeds. Spoon mixture into lined muffin pan and bake for 35 minutes or until tops start to turn golden brown. Remove from oven and let cool a few minutes before transferring to cooling rack. Serve each muffin with a sliver of grass-fed butter and a hard boiled egg to make it a balanced breakfast!

Note: These muffins are only moderately sweet. If transitioning to a whole foods diet, consider adding a drizzle of honey to each muffin on top of the sliced butter.

Nutrition Per Serving:
Calories 198, Total Fat 11g, Carbs 19g, Protein 8

Food as Medicine Tip:
Flour is a dead food! I try to avoid using flour from grain sources regardless of whether it is whole wheat or white. All flour is heat processed and highly refined, stripping the product of the nutrients of the grain from which it was derived. Then flour is synthetically re-enriched to provide some source of "nutrients" but often, they are not absorbable. I love using nut "flours" or nut meals in baking, as they provide more nutrients, with a delivery of essential fats and protein, rather than high-glycemic carbs!

Salads

Minty Beet Almond Salad with Goat Cheese
Watermelon, Cucumber & Feta Salad
Fresh Herb Tahini Salad
Kale Cannellini Salad
Mediterranean Chickpea Salad
Kale Aphrodisiac Salad
Zesty Citrus Cabbage Slaw
Carrot Beet Salad
Avocado, Cucumber & Tomato Salad
Ginger Pear Salad with Maple Glazed Salmon
Blueberry Pistachio Chevre Salad

MINTY BEET ALMOND SALAD
WITH GOAT CHEESE

MINTY BEET ALMOND SALAD WITH GOAT CHEESE

Makes:
6 Servings

Ingredients:
3 large beets, washed well and diced into 2-inch pieces
1 cup raw almonds
2 pears, cored and diced
1 large head leaf lettuce
4 cups baby kale, spinach, or green of choice
6 oz goat cheese
½ cup *Bright Minty Pepper Dressing*

Directions:
Preheat oven to 350°F. Place beets into a steamer basket in a medium-sized pot. Add about 2 inches of water. Cover and cook for about 45 minutes or until beets are fork tender. Drain off water and set aside to cool.
To roast the almonds, place them in a dry 8x8-inch baking dish and place into preheated oven. Bake for about 15 minutes. Remove from oven and place onto a plate to cool. Chop on a cutting board with a large knife once cooled.
Dice pears and set aside. Tear lettuce into pieces and chop greens then rinse and spin dry. Toss all ingredients, including beets, chopped almonds, pears, greens, and goat cheese in a bowl with dressing and serve immediately. If saving for lunches or meals throughout the week, separate ingredients and save dressing separately to toss just prior to eating.

Nutrition Per Serving:
Calories 259, Total Fat 11g, Carbs 22g , Protein 21g

Food as Medicine Tip:
A simple surprise, mint is able to shake up your salad and highlight beets without adding additional sweetener. In addition to a balance of flavors, this salad provides a potent boost of antioxidants and detoxifying compounds. The pears are rich in quercetin, an anti-inflammatory and anti-histimic ingredient, with unique bioflavonoids. Beets are rich in betalains which cleanse the blood and can work to dilate blood vessels thus reducing blood pressure!

WATERMELON, CUCUMBER
AND FETA SALAD

WATERMELON, CUCUMBER & FETA SALAD

Makes:
4 Servings

Ingredients:
4 cups watermelon, seeded and cubed
½ red onion, thinly sliced
1 medium cucumber, peeled and diced
¼ cup feta cheese, cut into ¼-inch cubes
3 Tbsp fresh mint, cut into thin ribbons
2 Tbsp pine nuts
3-4 cups arugula
¼ cup *Simple Balsamic Vinaigrette*

Directions:
In a large bowl, combine the cubed watermelon, cucumber, red onion, and feta cheese. Fold in the mint and pine nuts. Place on top of one cup arugula and drizzle with *Simple Balsamic Vinaigrette*. To make it a meal, top with 4-6 oz grilled chicken or roasted salmon.

Nutrition Per Serving:
Calories 263, Total Fat 19g, Carbs 20g, Protein 4g

Food as Medicine Tip:
Stay hydrated in summer by choosing fresh fruits and veggies, which help to volumize our intake and create a feeling of fullness. Watermelon and cucumber both boast particularly high water content, which helps to increase hydration, while holding over our appetite and also providing a nice delivery of antioxidants. Watermelon is high in the antioxidant lycopene, which helps to prevent certain types of cancer and is heart protective. It has also been shown to have blood pressure lowering effects and is a natural diuretic, aiding to reduce fluid retention. Cucumbers are also known for their hydrating effects and are high in B vitamins as well as potassium and fiber while providing anti-inflammatory support.

FRESH HERB TAHINI
SALAD

FRESH HERB TAHINI SALAD

Makes:
4 Servings

Ingredients:
4 cups assorted salad greens, torn into bite-sized pieces (choose from seasonal selections including lettuce, arugula, watercress, baby kale, chard, etc)
½ cup whole parsley leaves, flat Italian
¼ cup basil leaves, torn into bite-sized pieces
⅛ cup oregano leaves, chopped
½ cup *Tahini-Lemon Dressing*

Directions:
Toss ingredients in a bowl with ½ cup *Tahini-Lemon Dressing*. Serve as side salad or with protein of choice to make a complete meal.

Nutrition Per Serving:
Calories 173, Total Fat 8g, Carbs 16g, Protein 7g

Food as Medicine Tip:
Adding fresh herbs to green salads is a great way to contribute flavor with increased nutrients for a balanced diet! Simple flavors allow for a true appreciation for the bounty of the season. Fresh herbs are also very nutrient dense and can add antioxidant and detoxification support to any meal!

KALE CANNELLINI
SALAD

KALE CANNELLINI SALAD

Makes:
6 Servings

Ingredients:
1 bunch curly kale, washed, dried and thinly chopped
1 bunch Lacinato kale, washed, dried and thinly chopped
½ tsp sea salt
1 15 oz can cannellini beans, drained and rinsed
⅓ cup finely shredded Parmesan cheese
2 tsp Dijon mustard
2 Tbsp finely grated lemon zest
¼ cup freshly squeezed lemon juice
Freshly cracked black pepper
6 Tbsp extra-virgin olive oil

Directions:
Put chopped kale in large bowl and sprinkle with ½ tsp sea salt. Massage kale with hands to break down dense cell walls and soften greens for about 3 minutes. Add cannellini beans and Parmesan cheese. Set aside. In a small bowl, whisk together the mustard, lemon zest, lemon juice, pepper, and olive oil until thick, about 45 seconds. Drizzle some of the dressing over the kale. Taste, adjust seasoning, if needed then add more dressing, if desired. Serve as a side salad or add a protein, to make a complete meal.

Nutrition Per Serving:
Calories 239, Total Fat 15g, Carbs 12g, Protein 6g

Food as Medicine Tip:
Cannellini are one of the lowest glycemic beans, which means your blood sugar will not spike from the carbohydrates in the beans. Cannellini beans also metabolize slowly and provide steady energy for hours following their consumption. This slower absorption will stave off cravings for sugary foods and will also reduce your chances of developing cardiovascular disease, aiding in the reduction of plaque formation in arteries.

MEDITERRANEAN
CHICKPEA SALAD

MEDITERRANEAN CHICKPEA SALAD

Makes:
4 Servings

Ingredients:
1 15.5 oz can chickpeas or garbanzo beans, rinsed
1-2 heirloom tomatoes
⅛ cup Kalamata olives, pitted and sliced
Juice of 2 lemons, separated
2 Tbsp red wine vinegar
2 Tbsp olive oil
1 bunch fresh oregano, chopped
1 bunch fresh basil, chopped

Directions:
Mix chickpeas, tomatoes, and olives; toss in 2 Tbsp lemon juice. In a separate bowl, whisk remaining lemon juice, red wine vinegar, olive oil, and fresh mixed herbs. Pour over chickpea mixture. Toss to combine well and allow flavors to combine for 30 minutes in fridge prior to serving.

Note: To make a complete balanced meal, top with your choice of protein; chicken or tuna would be perfect.

Nutrition Per Serving:
Calories 169, Total Fat 11, Carbs 14g, Protein 5g

Food as Medicine Tip:
Legumes are great for the heart and may prevent cancer!
A cup of cooked beans a day can lower your total cholesterol by up to 10% in 6 weeks. A study conducted at the University of Kentucky has shown that only three weeks of increased bean intake (¾ cup daily) lowered the men's cholesterol by an average of 19%. This reduces the risk of heart attack by almost 40%! Legumes, as a fiber source, help to move food and toxins through our bodies and decrease the risk of various types of cancer while regulating our GI tract.

KALE APHRODISIAC
SALAD

KALE APHRODISIAC SALAD

Makes:
4 Servings

Ingredients:
1 bunch lacinato kale, stemmed and chiffonade (roll leaves and slice into thin ribbons)
½ teaspoon sea salt
2 Tbsp olive oil
2 Tbsp lemon juice
2 tsp raw, unfiltered honey
black pepper, to taste
2 watermelon radishes, thinly sliced into half moons
1 avocado, cubed
1 cup pomegranate seeds
½ cup walnuts, roasted

Directions:
Place the chiffonade kale in a bowl and sprinkle with sea salt. Massage the kale until it begins to soften. In a separate bowl, whisk together olive oil, lemon, and honey with black pepper and sea salt to taste. Massage leaves in the dressing mixture.
Fold in the radishes and avocado. Top with walnuts and pomegranate seeds.

Nutrition Per Serving:
Calories 303, Total Fat 23g, Carbs 22g, Protein 8g

Food as Medicine Tip:
Researchers have identified over 45 different flavonoids in kale; kaempferol and quercetin top the list. These flavonoids combine both antioxidant, anti-inflammatory, and anti-cancer benefits in a way that gives kale a leading dietary role. Kale can provide great benefit in combating chronic inflammation and oxidative stress. In addition, kale is now recognized for its comprehensive support for the body's detoxification system. Raw kale is full of vitamin K, A, C, manganese, fiber, copper, tryptophan, and calcium amongst many other nutrients. Massaging your kale aids in the activation and absorption of the nutrients available while reducing the bitterness and aiding in mechanical break-down. Avocado was referred to as testicle by the Aztecs as they grew in bunches of two on trees. Rich in vitamin A and vitamin E, avocado promotes healthy skin and minerals support testosterone production for healthy sex drive. Pomegranate has been compared to ovaries in structural comparison and honey aids in the balance of estrogen dominance.

ZESTY CITRUS
CABBAGE SLAW

ZESTY CITRUS CABBAGE SLAW

Makes:
4 Servings

Ingredients:
½ head green cabbage, shredded
½ head red cabbage, shredded
4 carrots, shredded
½ cup *Zesty Citrus Dressing*
1 mango, sliced into thin matchsticks
1 avocado, cubed
1 bunch green onion tops, thinly sliced
1 bunch cilantro, stemmed and leaves torn

Directions:
Combine cabbage and carrots in a large bowl and mix well until evenly distributed. Toss mixture with Zesty Citrus Dressing, then gently fold in the mango and avocado to ensure not to bruise or over mash. Sprinkle in green onions and most of cilantro reserving some for garnish. Refrigerate about 30 minutes to allow flavors to meld. When ready to serve, garnish with remaining cilantro.

Nutrition Per Serving:
Calories 319, Total Fat 20g, Carbs 36g, Protein 4g

Food as Medicine Tip:
Cilantro is great for detoxification of heavy metals! Cilantro was found to suppress lead accumulation in rats, due to its chelation abilities and is even being studied as a water purifier. This property of metal chelation paired with the rich source of detoxifying sulfur-containing compounds in the cabbage provide a synergistic cleansing effect. Pairing these detox nutrients with the citrus dressing, which is rich in vitamin C aids in the recycling and building of the most potent antioxidant, glutathione; working to ultimately reduce free radical activity.

CARROT BEET
SALAD

CARROT BEET SALAD

Makes:
4 Servings

Ingredients:
1 orange, juiced (about 3 Tbsp)
2 tsp lemon juice
2 tsp olive oil
1 tsp fresh minced ginger
¼ tsp sea salt
1 cup peeled and shredded carrot
1 cup peeled and shredded beets
2 Tbsp chopped mint

Directions:
Whisk orange juice, lemon juice, olive oil, ginger, and sea salt until combined. Drizzle carrots with half of the dressing and toss. Add beets and pour on remaining dressing. Fold in chopped mint and allow to set in refrigerator at least 30 minutes before serving.

Nutrition Per Serving:
Calories 47, Total Fat 3g, Carbs 6g, Protein 2g

Food as Medicine Tip:
When you purchase beets it's like getting a two items for the price of one! Don't trash the greens! The greens of beets provide a nice delicate flavor and can be eaten raw, sautéed, or braised. Beet greens are high in vitamin K, which has blood clotting properties and bone strengthening benefits as well, preventing osteoporosis. Beet greens are very high in iron and have a higher nutritional value than the beetroot itself. Try including them in smoothies, stir-frys, and braising them down in bone broth and balsamic for a nourishing side dish.

AVOCADO, CUCUMBER, TOMATO SALAD

AVOCADO, CUCUMBER, & TOMATO SALAD

Makes:
6 Servings

Ingredients:
1 avocado, pitted and diced
½ cup diced red onion
1 cup of cherry tomatoes, cut in half
1 cucumber, peeled and seeded, cut into chunks
2 Tbsp olive oil
4 tsp red wine vinegar
pinch of sea salt
dash of pepper

Directions:
Put avocado, onion, tomatoes, and cucumber in a bowl. In a separate bowl, whisk olive oil, red wine vinegar, sea salt, pepper. Pour dressing over salad. Stir lightly with a wooden spoon so you won't tear up the avocado. Serve 1 cup salad with vinaigrette on top of a bed made with 2-3 cups Romaine lettuce. The dressing may seem too tangy if you taste it before adding it to the salad, but it mellows out after it is stirred into the veggies.
Optional: to make this a complete meal, add 4 oz canned skipjack tuna.

Nutrition Per Serving:
(1 cup salad over 2 cups lettuce) Calories 102, Total Fat 8g, Carbs 6g, Protein 2g

Nutrition Per Serving (with 4 oz tuna):
Calories 306, Total Fat 15g, Carbs 6g, Protein 30g

Food as Medicine Tip:
Avocados are higher in potassium than bananas. They also offer a great source of vitamin E, K, B6, and folate. They have a healthy fatty acid profile that has demonstrated through research to protect against prostate and breast cancer as well as heart disease.

GINGER PEAR SALAD WITH MAPLE
GLAZED SALMON

GINGER PEAR SALAD WITH MAPLE GLAZED SALMON

Makes:
1 Serving

Ingredients:
1 Tbsp pecans, roasted
½ pear, sliced
3 cups mixed salad greens
2 Tbsp *Zingy Ginger Dressing*
4-5 oz *Maple Glazed Wild Salmon*

Directions:
Combine roasted pecans, pear slices, and mixed greens in a bowl. Toss with *Zingy Ginger Dressing* and plate with one piece *Maple Glazed Wild Salmon*.

Note: to roast pecans, place on dry baking sheet in oven at 375°F for 10-15 minutes until aromatic, shake halfway through roasting process to prevent over browning.

Nutrition Per Serving:
Calories 409, Total Fat 19g, Carbs 33g, Protein 25g

Food as Medicine Tip:
Pecans are rich in phytochemical substances that help to support detoxification including ellagic acid, vitamin E, beta-carotene, and lutein. These compounds play an important role in removing toxic-free radicals, preventing disease and infections. Ellagic acid has properties which inhibit DNA binding of certain carcinogens, protecting the human body from cancers.

BLUEBERRY PISTACHIO
CHEVRE SALAD

BLUEBERRY PISTACHIO CHEVRE SALAD

Makes:
4 Servings

Ingredients:
For the salad:
10 cups Local spring mix
⅓ small red onion, thinly sliced
1 cup blueberries
1 pound shredded chicken, combination white and dark meat
½ cup *Blueberry Vinaigrette*
½ cup chevre
¼ cup pistachios

Directions:
Toss greens, red onion, blueberries, and chicken in *Blueberry Vinaigrette*. Serve in 4 portions topped with 2 Tbsp chevre and 1 Tbsp pistachios.

Nutrition Per Serving:
Calories 467, Total Fat 28g, Carbs 13g, Protein 41g

Food as Medicine Tip:
Blueberries are rich in antioxidant phytonutrients called anthocyanidins, which can neutralize free radical damage that leads to cataracts, glaucoma, varicose veins, hemorrhoids, peptic ulcers, heart disease and cancer. Pairing the sweet fruit with goat cheese is an excellent way to promote stable blood sugar. Goat cheese is easier to digest than other cheeses and contains Vitamin K2, which helps to decalcify arteries and decrease the risk of both cardiovascular disease risk and osteoporosis! This salad is a meal in itself with the addition of shredded chicken, which is also a good source of K2 in its dark meat. Be sure to choose pasture-raised, organic chicken for a clean source that is low in toxicity and rich in nutrients.

Soups

Black Bean Soup
Turkey Wild Rice Soup
Curried Pumpkin Soup
Tex-Mex Chicken Soup
Avocado Cucumber Soup
Cauliflower Chowder
Tomato Basil Soup

BLACK BEAN
SOUP

BLACK BEAN SOUP

Makes:
6 Servings

Ingredients:
1½ Tbsp olive oil
1 yellow onion, chopped
4-5 carrots, chopped
4 garlic cloves, chopped
1 Tbsp ground cumin
½ to 1 chopped jalapeño chile with seeds, divided
32-ounce can black beans, drained and rinsed (look for Eden brand made with Kombu or soak dried beans and cook with a piece of Kombu seaweed)
1 15 oz can organic fire-roasted tomatoes
3 cups bone broth - see recipe on pg. 212 (or chicken stock for lighter option)
1 tsp sea salt
Chopped fresh cilantro
½ cup full fat Greek yogurt, divided into 6 Servings
½ cup pico de gallo, divided into 6 Servings
Optional: Spinach or Baby Kale; Optional: Rotisserie chicken

Directions:
Heat oil in heavy large stock pot over medium heat. Add onion, carrots, and garlic; sauté until vegetables begin to soften, about 6 minutes. Mix in cumin and 1 tablespoon jalapeño. Add rinsed beans, tomatoes with juice, and broth; bring soup to boil. Reduce heat to medium, cover, and cook until carrots are tender, about 15 minutes. Transfer 3 cups of soup to blender and puree until smooth. Return puree to pot. Simmer soup until slightly thickened, about 15 minutes. Season to taste with salt and remaining jalapeño, if desired. Garnish each bowl with a handful of chopped cilantro, dollop of Greek yogurt, and large spoonful of pico de gallo. Optional: place 1-2 cups raw greens in your bowl before serving to boost nutrients and promote more volume at lower calories! If consuming as a complete meal, top with shredded rotisserie chicken or white fish!

Nutrition Per Serving:
(without chicken): Calories 181, Total Fat 4g, Carbs 32g, Protein 12g

Food as Medicine Tip:
This soup offers detoxifying support with soluble fiber from beans. Legumes or beans have a lot of anti-nutrients that cause gas, bloating, and block our ability to absorb the vitamins and minerals they otherwise provide. I recommend soaking beans overnight about 8-12 hours in filtered water, then draining off the soak water and boiling water on the stovetop, when adding in the soaked beans, I also throw in a 2- to 3-inch piece of Kombu seaweed. Kombu helps to break down the phytates (anti-nutrients) reducing gas and increasing nutritional density. Also sea vegetables have 10-20x the minerals as land vegetables due to the mineral deficiency in our soils. Kombu also aids in tonifying the thyroid gland with iodine a trace mineral that many Americans are deficient in.

TURKEY WILD RICE SOUP

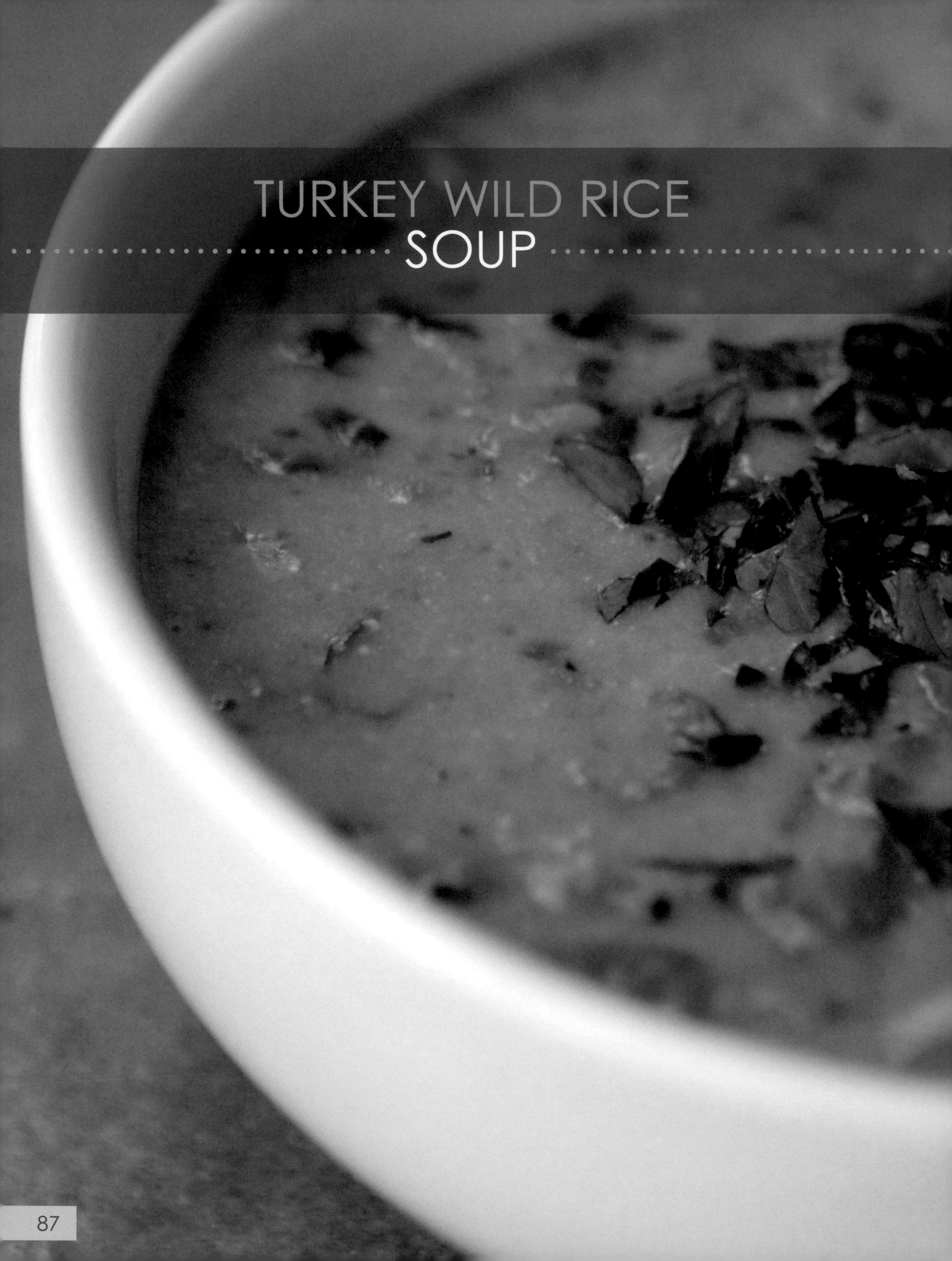

TURKEY WILD RICE SOUP

Makes:
6 Servings

Ingredients:
1 Tbsp extra-virgin olive oil
2 cups sliced crimini (baby bella) mushrooms
2 cups celery, chopped
2 cups carrots, chopped
½ cup shallots, chopped
¼ tsp sea salt
¼ tsp freshly ground pepper
6 cups *Chicken Bone Broth* (see recipe on pg. 212); reserve 4 oz
1½ cups quick-cooking wild rice
2 Tbsp arrowroot
20 oz deli turkey, cut into ½-inch thick slices and cubed (about 2 cups)* see below
2 Tbsp chopped fresh parsley
½ cup Greek yogurt

Directions:
Heat oil in a large saucepan over medium heat. Add mushrooms, celery, carrots, and shallots to cook, stirring occasionally until softened, about 5 minutes. Add salt and pepper, stirring, for 2 minutes more. Add broth (reserving 4 oz) and bring to a boil, scraping up any browned bits with wooden spoon. Add rice and reduce heat to a simmer.
Cover and continue cooking until the rice is tender, 7-10 minutes. In a small bowl, combine arrowroot and the remaining 4 oz broth to create a slurry. To thicken the soup add arrowroot mixture, stir until well incorporated into pot and soup thickens. Stir in turkey and cook until heated through, about 2 minutes more. Add parsley and remove from heat or reduce to low simmer. Spoon a couple scoops of Greek yogurt into each bowl and fill with 2 cups of soup. Garnish with fresh parsley.

Note: For selecting deli turkey, look for the "in-house roast" from your natural foods grocery store. This will be made from whole turkey breast without added binders/fillers.

Nutrition Per Serving:
Calories 219, Total Fat 4g, Carbs 19g, Protein 25g

Food as Medicine Tip:
Soup is a great vehicle for volumetrics or focusing on satiety with minimal calorie impact. By using bone broth in your recipe rather than packaged broth, you will boost the nutritional density and increase digestive support with more L-glutamine and collagen. Add a couple cups of mixed greens to the bottom of your bowl for additional antioxidants and fiber.

CURRIED PUMPKIN
SOUP

CURRIED PUMPKIN SOUP

Makes:
5 Servings

Ingredients:
1 Tbsp butter
1 large yellow onion, chopped
1 shallot, chopped (about ⅓ cup)
2 cups chopped celery
1 apple, chopped
2 Tbsp mild curry powder
3 cups *Chicken Bone Broth* (see recipe on pg. 212)
2 cups pumpkin puree (if canned ensure unsweetened and unseasoned)
¼ tsp sea salt, more to taste
3 whole bay leaves
⅓ cup full fat, canned coconut milk
1 Tbsp honey
Greek yogurt and chives, for garnish
Roasted pumpkin seeds, for garnish

Directions:
Melt the butter in a medium-size soup pot. Stir in the onion, shallot, celery, and apple. Sauté the ingredients over medium-high heat, until the onion is translucent and ingredients begin to brown, about 6 minutes. Stir in the curry powder and sauté the mixture for another 2 minutes. Stir in 1 cup of chicken broth and cook another minute.

Pour the contents of the pot into a blender or food processor, add the pumpkin, and puree the soup until it's smooth. Pour mixture back into the pot, then stir in the remaining chicken broth, salt, and bay leaf. Set the soup over medium-high heat and bring it to a simmer, stirring occasionally. After 5 minutes, stir in the coconut milk and honey. Taste the soup, adding more salt or honey if necessary to get the desired balance of sweet and savory. Simmer soup for 2 minutes more to combine flavors then remove the soup from the heat, and serve warm. Garnish each bowl with a dollop of Greek yogurt and a sprinkling of chopped chives and pumpkin seeds.

Nutrition Per Serving:
Calories 151, Total Fat 6g, Carbs 18g, Protein 8g

Food as Medicine Tip:
Turmeric is one of the most abundant spices in curry powder, and one of the organic components of turmeric is curcumin. Researchers have connected curcumin to a plethora of health related benefits including a reduction in inflammation and joint pain, cancer prevention, heart health benefits as well as prevention in the formation of plaque that free radicals deposit in the neural pathways of the brain, therefore reducing cognitive decline with Alzheimer's disease.

TEX-MEX CHICKEN
SOUP

TEX-MEX CHICKEN SOUP

Makes:
6 Servings

Ingredients:
1½ Tbsp olive oil
1 cup chopped onion
3 garlic cloves, minced
1 red bell pepper, chopped
1 jalapeño, seeded and minced
1 Tbsp chili powder
1½ tsp crushed red pepper
½ tsp salt
½ tsp ground cumin
½ tsp black pepper
2 large tomatoes, chopped
3 cups shredded rotisserie chicken
4 cups *Chicken Bone Broth* (see recipe on pg. 212)
1 15 oz can no-salt added black beans, rinsed
¼ cup fresh chopped cilantro
3 oz queso fresco, crumbled
8 lime wedges

Directions:
Heat a dutch oven oven or stockpot over medium heat. Add oil, onion, garlic, bell pepper, and jalapeno, then sauté 3 minutes, stirring occassionally. Add chili powder, red pepper, salt, cumin, and black pepper stirring to combine allowing to sauté another 2 minutes to combine flavors. Add tomatoes and chicken, coating in seasoning with spoon, followed by broth and beans. Bring to a boil. Reduce heat to a moderate simmer, stiring the pot to prevent any browning, then cover with lid and simmer 10-15 minutes to allow flavors to meld. After 15 minutes, if the soup has thinned too much, remove lid and simmer an additional 3-5 minutes to thicken and reduce. Remove from heat and serve in bowls. Top each bowl with cilantro and queso. Serve with a lime wedge.

Nutrition Per Serving:
Calories 282, Total Fat 13g, Carbs 12g, Protein 29g

Food as Medicine Tip:
Lycopene is increased in the cooking process! There are often debates about the most nutritionally dense way to prepare foods: cooked, raw, steamed, boiled, etc. It is optimal to do both a cooked and raw preparation for optimal intake of a variety of antioxidants, vitamins, and phytocompounds. Lycopene, the antioxidant in red vegetables and fruits is increased with heat processing. When eating foods raw, it is important to include an acid and a fat for optimal nutritional absorption.

AVOCADO CUCUMBER
SOUP

AVOCADO CUCUMBER SOUP

Makes:
2 Servings

Ingredients:
1 cucumber (peeled and de-seeded plus additional cuke for garnish)
1 Tbsp onion minced
1 avocado, peeled
1 Tbsp olive oil
1 Tbsp lemon juice
1 Tbsp Braggs raw apple cider vinegar
¼ tsp sea salt
¼ tsp chili powder
1 dash of cayenne pepper
1 cup water

Directions:
Throw cucumber, onion, avocao, oil, lemon juice, apple cider vinegar and water in blender. Puree on high speed until smooth. Blend in salt, chili powder, cayenne and water. Serve, garnishing with extra cucumber cubes and smoked paprika if desired. Optional: top with kale chips as garnish.

Nutrition Per Serving:
Calories 193, Total Fat 18 g, Carbs 8g, Protein 2g

Food as Medicine Tip:
Capsaicin is responsible for giving cayenne and other peppers their heat. This compound is known for increasing thermogenisis in the body by promoting the body to burn fat for fuel. Capsaicin is also known to prevent a decline in metabolic rate that typically follows weight loss.

CAULIFLOWER
CHOWDER

CAULIFLOWER CHOWDER

Makes:
6 Servings

Ingredients:
4 slices pasture-raised, nitrite-free bacon, crumbled
2 Tbsp butter
2 cloves garlic, minced
1 cup leeks, finely chopped, green parts reserved for bone broth
2 carrots, diced
2 stalks celery, diced
1 head cauliflower, chopped into small florets
3 sprigs thyme
1 bay leaf
½ tsp ground cumin
¼ tsp ground coriander
6 cups bone broth
1 cup full fat, canned coconut milk
sea salt, to taste
black pepper, to taste
2 Tbsp parsley, chopped
2 green onions, sliced thinly

Directions:
In a large skillet, cook the bacon until crispy. Set aside on a paper towel lined plate.
Melt the butter in a large stockpot. Add the garlic, leeks, carrot, celery and a generous pinch of sea salt. Cook until tender and leeks are translucent. Add the cumin, coriander, thyme and bay leaf and cook until fragrant.
Add in the cauliflower florets and cook until tender. Add the bone broth. Bring to a boil, then reduce the heat and simmer 15-20 minutes with the lid off. When the cauliflower is tender, add in the coconut milk and season to taste with the salt and pepper. Cook 3-5 minutes longer, then remove from heat.
Garnish with chopped bacon, parsley and green onions, and a sprinkling of black pepper.
Note: Cooking with the lid off allows the noxious gas to escape, reducing gas and bloat and helps to eliminate the smell that is characteristic of sulfur.

Nutrition Per Serving:
256 Calories, Total Fat 15g, Carbs 13g, Protein 11g

Food as Medicine Tip:
Food as Medicine Tip: Cauliflower has a mild and sweet flavor and can be prepared in a variety of ways including roasted, sautéed, steamed or even chopped as a rice substitute or mashed, as a potato substitute. Cauliflower has a variety of nutritional benefits, one being cancer prevention and another being Cauliflower's detox capabilities. Cauliflower contains active compounds needed for both phase 1 and phase 2 detox activities as well glucosinates that help to activate enzymes needed for detoxification. A great source of vitamin K, Cauliflower also fights cancer via anti-inflammatory effects.

TOMATO BASIL
SOUP

TOMATO BASIL SOUP

Makes:
2 Servings

Ingredients:
3 heirloom tomatoes, about 3 cups
6 basil leaves or more if desired
1 celery stalk
2 cloves garlic
⅛ cup onion
Juice of 1 lime
¼ cup or so olive oil (may reduce for caloric purposes if looking to use as a side dish)
1 tsp sea salt
1 Tbsp fresh oregano or 1 tsp dry
black pepper, to taste

Directions:
Mix up in food processor in short bursts. Garnish with avocado cubes. Yum!

Nutrition Per Serving:
Calories 274, Total Fat 27 g, Carbs 11g, Protein 2g

Food as Medicine Tip:
Fats and acids are two important and synergistic components of creating a flavorful, balanced dish. When blended properly, they form a beautiful harmony, with our taste buds working to round out flavors and make ingredients sing. Nutritionally, fats and acids ensure optimal absorption of nutrients. The olive oil in this recipe increases the absorption of fat soluble vitamins and antioxidants such as beta carotene and lycopene. Adding acid as seen through the ascorbic acid or vitamin C in the lime juice aids in absorption of minerals and activating antioxidants.

Snacks

Parm Crisps 3-Ways
Wild Salmon Roll-ups
Greek Yogurt Dip with Raw Veggies
Beet Hummus with Vegetable Spears
Simple Caprese Stack Up
Simple Dressed Avocado
Kale Chips
Herb Roasted Nuts
Blueberry Pumpkin Seed Oat Bars

PARM CRISPS
3-WAYS

PARM CRISPS 3-WAYS

Makes:
4 Servings; 1 oz each

Ingredients:
4 oz Parmesan*, shredded thinly
Choose your flavor enhancer(s) below:
Option 1: 2 tsp red pepper flakes
Option 2: ½ tsp garlic powder, ½ tsp dill, ¼ tsp onion powder, 1 tsp black pepper
Option 3: 1 tsp finely chopped rosemary and ¼ tsp pepper

Directions:
Preheat oven to 300°F. Mix shredded Parmesan with your choice of flavor enhancer. Using a tablespoon, scoop 1 Tbsp then mound on a silicone pad or greased parchment paper-lined cookie sheet. Scoop mounds into three, 4-column rows and flatten each mound with the back of a spoon. Ensure Parmesan formations are not touching. Bake on middle rack for 5-7 minutes until golden brown. Store air tight.

Note: Shred your Parmesan yourself with a microplane or shredder to avoid anti-caking additives in pre-shredded, store bought cheeses.

Nutrition Per Serving:
Calories 135, Total Fat 8g, Carbs 1 g, Protein 11g

Food as Medicine Tip:
Cholesterol as medicine? Yes! Cholesterol is present in every cell membrane, helping to keep nutrients in the cell to be used by its mitochondria "energy factories" to provide fuel for the body and prevent undesired toxins from getting into the cells! Cholesterol also works as a steroid hormone building block, aiding in the production of serotonin, vitamin D, testosterone, coenzyme Q10, and other vital compounds. Cholesterol also has antioxidant properties that can protect the body from free radicals. We are learning more about the role of dietary fat and are starting to remove the blinders from the cholesterol myths that have long been misleading and may have led to harm.
The removal of eggs from the breakfast table and replacement with sugary cereal has contributed to less satiety while accelerating the cardiovascular, diabetic, and obesity epidemic in our country! Heart disease is caused by inflammation, not dietary cholesterol. Cholesterol does play a role in plaque formation but only after an injury has occurred in the lining of the vessel. In this way, blaming cholesterol for heart disease is similar to blaming a firefighter for the cause of a fire! These delicious crunchy salty crisps satisfy cravings without the carbohydrate overload. We like using them with eggs to "soup" up the yolks, to top a salad or soup for a desired texture change, or as a mid-day snack!

WILD SALMON
ROLL-UPS

WILD SALMON ROLL-UPS

Makes:
2 Servings

Ingredients:
4 oz smoked salmon
2 oz cream cheese
1 tsp kelp powder
1 Tbsp fresh basil or parsley, chopped

Directions:
Peel apart salmon pieces and lay flat. Spread each piece with about a teaspoon of cream cheese, then sprinkle kelp powder on top of cream cheese. Roll up and top with fresh herbs.

Nutrition Per Serving:
Calories 143, Total Fat 8g, Carbs 0g, Protein 16g

Food as Medicine Tip:
Wild Salmon is full of heart healthy, Omega 3 fatty acids and lean body mass fueling protein! Cured Salmon makes for a quick and easy snack or dinner and can be found prepackaged in the deli section of the super market!

GREEK YOGURT DIP WITH
RAW VEGGIES

GREEK YOGURT DIP
WITH RAW VEGGIES

Makes:
4 Servings

Ingredients:
2 cups Greek yogurt
3 Tbsp fresh parsley, chopped
2 Tbsp fresh dill, chopped
2 Tbsp chives, chopped
1 clove garlic, finely minced
1 Tbsp lemon juice
¼ tsp garlic powder
¼ tsp onion powder
pinch sea salt
pinch black pepper

Directions:
In a medium bowl, combine all of the ingredients. Mix well, folding the herbs into the yogurt until combined. Season to taste. Serve with vegetable crudités.

Nutrition Per Serving:
Calories 123, Total Fat 5g, Carbs 10g, Protein 11g

Food as Medicine Tip:
Greek Yogurt makes this dip feel like a rich, creamy treat, while adding beneficial probiotics to your snack! Over 80% of our immune system is regulated by the gut, so incorporating probiotic food sources into your daily plan is a great way to ensure the bacteria in your body is working to protect and regulate vs. wreak havoc in your gut. Studies have shown, eating foods rich in probiotics can lead to an improved immune response by increasing the body's white blood cell count. Greek yogurt is also a protein powerhouse, with at least 15g in a 6oz serving! Pair this dip with a plethora of fresh, crunchy vegetables to get the most volume with the least amount of calories. This concept of volumetrics can help you feel satiated with an abundance of foods, while keeping your intake in check! This recipe is a great idea for your next social gathering - your friends will thank you for it!

ROASTED BEET HUMMUS WITH
VEGETABLE SPEARS

ROASTED BEET HUMMUS
WITH VEGETABLE SPEARS

Makes:
6 Servings (½ cup each)

Ingredients:
2 small roasted beets, about ¾ cup
1 Tbsp olive oil
1 15 oz can (1¾ cups) cooked chickpeas, drained
zest of 1 lemon
1 Tbsp lemon juice, about the juice of 1 lemon
¼ tsp sea salt
2 cloves garlic, minced
2 Tbsp tahini
¼ cup extra virgin olive oil
vegetable spears of choice for serving: carrots, bell peppers, jicama, broccoli

Directions:
Roast beets by cutting them into quarters, lightly coating in olive oil and roasting at 375°F for about 30 minutes until tender. Let beets cool and then add to food processor using standard metal "s" blade and blend until smooth. Then add ingredients chickpeas through tahini, and continue to run food processor until smooth. With blade running, pour in olive oil at steady stream to incorporate well and create a fluffy texture. Serve with vegetable spears.

Nutrition Per Serving:
Calories 202, Total Fat 12g, Carbs 29g, Protein 7g

Food as Medicine Tip:
Beets are a rich source of antioxidants and phytocompounds. The most widely researched and medicinal compounds in beets are betalains, shown to provide antioxidant, anti-inflammatory, and detoxification support. Scientists have identified these compounds as having the ability to fight tumors in the body. Beets increase nitric oxide in the body, which dilates vessels and lowers blood pressure. Lutein and zeaxanthin are two carotenoids found in the greens of beets but not in the root! Eat the greens to gain the vitamins, minerals, folate, and carotenoid benefits of disease prevention, especially for eye health!

SIMPLE CAPRESE
STACK UP

SIMPLE CAPRESE STACK UP

Makes:
4 Servings

Ingredients:
2 large heirloom tomatoes
4 oz fresh mozzarella cheese
3 Tbsp fresh basil, cut into thin ribbons
drizzle balsamic vinegar and olive oil
pinch sea salt

Directions:
Slice the tomatoes into ¼-inch thick slices. Do the same with the mozzarella.
Stack 3 slices of tomato with two slices of mozzarella in between.
Drizzle with balsamic vinegar and olive oil and sprinkle with the sea salt. Top with the basil.

Nutrition Per Serving:
Calories 204, Fat 18g, Carbs 3g, Protein 7g

Food as Medicine Tip:
This simple salad comes together in a matter of minutes and is an instant classic. Tomatoes contain high levels of potassium and chromium, which can help to stabilize blood sugar and ward off sugar cravings. Ideally we like to consume tomatoes prepared a variety of ways, both raw and cooked, for the best balance of nutrients. Choose grass-fed mozzarella, which contains K2 to decalcify arteries and decrease the risk of both cardiovascular disease risk and osteoporosis! Basil packs a nice antioxidant punch and is also an aphrodisiac. Serve alongside 4-6 ounces protein of your choice for a balanced meal.

SIMPLE DRESSED
AVOCADO

SIMPLE DRESSED AVOCADO

Makes:
2 Servings

Ingredients:
2-3 tsp jalapeño, chopped
1 Tbsp red onion, chopped
1 tsp chili powder
generous pinch of sea salt
1 Tbsp lemon juice
2 tsp avocado or olive oil
1 Tbsp pepitas (hulled pumpkin seeds)
2 Tbsp cilantro, chopped
½ avocado

Directions:
Combine together jalapeño through lemon juice and then whisk in oil with a steady pour, whisking to emulsify. Fold in pepitas and cilantro. Spoon on top of a ½ pitted avocado. For a quick snack, serve as-is and eat with a spoon. If looking to tackle hunger, volumize this dish by adding sprouts or leafy greens of choice.

Nutrition Per Serving:
Calories 124, Total Fat 12 g, Carbs 4g, Protein 1 g

Food as Medicine Tip:
A fun take on Tex-Mex flavor profiles provides support for metabolism and detox. The avocado contributes B vitamins and fatty acids that aid to manage stress response and reduce excess stress hormone, cortisol while the spice and zing of onions aids to boost metabolism and detoxification. This is a great snack to curb cravings and aid in managing mood.

KALE
CHIPS

KALE CHIPS

Makes:
4 Servings

RANCH	**BLACK PEPPER PARMESAN**
Ingredients:	**Ingredients:**
1 bunch kale leaves, stemmed and torn into 2-inch pieces	1 bunch kale leaves, stemmed and torn into 2- inch pieces
½ Tbsp extra virgin olive oil or melted coconut oil	½ Tbsp extra virgin olive oil or melted coconut oil
1 Tbsp nutritional yeast	¼ cup Parmesan cheese, finely grated
1 tsp dried chives	¼ tsp black pepper
½ tsp dried parsley	¼ tsp sea salt
¼ tsp onion powder	
¼ tsp garlic powder	
¼ tsp dried dill	
¼ tsp sea salt	

Directions:
Preheat the oven to 300°F. Line a baking sheet with parchment paper.
Place kale in a large bowl. Add in the oil and massage until all of the pieces are covered. Sprinkle with the seasoning combination of your choice. Spread the kale in a single layer on the baking sheet, be careful not to overcrowd as this will steam the kale.
Bake for 15-20 minutes until crispy. Cool for 3 minutes and enjoy!

Nutrition Per Serving:
Calories 95, Total Fat 4g, Carbs 10g, Protein 5g

Food as Medicine Tip:
Kale chips are a great way to satisfy a craving for a salty, crunchy snack while being low in both calories and carbohydrates. Even when baked into crispy chips, kale maintains its superfood status and is packed with Vitamins A, C, and K as well as calcium and fiber. Kale can also help to combat chronic inflammation and oxidative damage, reducing the risk of cardiovascular disease, diabetes and cancer. Baking the kale also deactivates goitrogens, which can affect thyroid hormone function and are not advisable to be consumed by people with existing thyroid conditions. Ideally, it is best to consume kale prepared a variety of ways, both raw and cooked, to reap the benefits of all of its nutrients!

HERB ROASTED
NUTS

HERB ROASTED NUTS

Makes:
15 Servings, about ¼ cup each

Ingredients:
2 cups almonds
2 cups pecans
1 cup cashews
1 cup chopped Brazil nuts
⅓ cup grade b maple syrup
pinch cayenne
2 Tbsp coconut oil
1 Tbsp each: chopped fresh rosemary, basil, thyme
generous pinch of sea salt

Directions:
Preheat oven to 300°F. Mix nuts and set aside. In a separate bowl mix maple syrup, cayenne, coconut oil, and herbs. Stir in nuts and ensure all are equally coated. Spread on unbleached parchment paper over baking sheet and sprinkle with sea salt. Place baking sheet at center of preheated oven, bake for 15 minutes. Then move baking sheet to top rack of oven and bake an additional additional 10 min on top rack until liquid evaporates. Cool and store in air-tight mason jars. Consider filling ribbon-tied jars, and giving as a gift.

Nutrition Per Serving:
Calories 238, Total Fat 21g, Carbs 9g, Protein 6g

Food as Medicine Tip:
Nuts are a great source of healthy fats, paired with protein and a moderate dose of carbs. They are correlated with increased life expectancy, possibly due to their content of monoun-saturated fats, which improve vessel health, and arginine which aids in dilating blood vessels, decreasing blood pressure. They also provide a rich source of fat soluble antioxidants which aid in fighting against cancer and cognitive decline.

BLUEBERRY PUMPKIN SEED
OAT BARS

BLUEBERRY PUMPKIN SEED OAT BARS

Makes:
12 Servings

Ingredients:
½ cup raw, unfiltered honey
2 tsp vanilla extract
¼ tsp sea salt
½ cup almond butter (optional sunbutter if making nut-free)
2-3 scoops *Naturally Nourished Grass-fed Whey Protein*
1-2 oz filtered water
1½ cups rolled oats
¼ cup cacao nibs (may omit if too bitter for kids or replace with 2 Tbsp cacao powder)
½ cup pumpkin seeds
½ cup dried blueberries

Directions:
Combine the honey, vanilla, salt, and almond butter in a medium sized saucepan and bring to a simmer. Reduce heat to a low simmer and cook for about four minutes, stirring continuously to prevent burning. Once well blended, remove from heat and stir in whey. As there will be variations in viscosity of almond butter and honey, consider adding water, 1 tsp at a time, to mixture to meet the desired thickness of maple syrup, continuously whisking to incorporate. In a large bowl, combine oats, nibs, pumpkin seeds, and blueberries. Pour the liquid honey mixture over the oat mixture and combine until well mixed. Press mixture into a greased 9-inch pan and pat down with wet hands. Chill in fridge for an hour, or until firm. Then cut into 12 bars.

Nutrition Per Serving:
Calories 277, Total Fat 13g, Carbs 33g, Protein 11

Food as Medicine Tip:
This recipe satisfies your sweet tooth while keeping your blood sugar levels on track! The soluble fiber in the rolled oats works to slow the breakdown of carbohydrates into sugar while lowering cholesterol levels. Almond butter serves as a healthy fat and protein source to sustain energy levels. Pumpkin seeds provide zinc for added support in blood sugar metabolism while boosting immune health.

Entrees

Seafood Entrees
Grilled Shrimp Skewers
Pesto Crusted Halibut
Asparagus and Prosciutto Saute with Seared Scallops
Maple Glazed Salmon
Miso Glazed Salmon with Gingery Vegetable Stir-fry

Red Meat Entrees
Colorful Soba Noodle Salad with Seared Buffalo
Seared Sirloin with Cherry Wine Reduction
Spaghetti Squash Casserole
Spicy Grass-fed Beef Stir-fry
Garlicky Kale Stuffed Grass-fed Meatloaf
Slow Cooker Carnitas
Bourbon Peach Tenderloin

Poultry Entrees
Chicken Piccata
Pesto Turkey Meatballs and Roasted Vegetables
Tarragon Roasted Chicken and Vegetables
Mustard Chicken Thighs
Pan Seared Chicken with Tomato Jam
Curry Mango Chicken Salad
Broccoli Chicken Dijon

GRILLED SHRIMP
SKEWERS

GRILLED SHRIMP SKEWERS

Makes:
7 Servings, 3 shrimp per skewer

Ingredients:
4 Tbsp melted butter or ghee
2 Tbsp lime juice
1 Tbsp tamari, gluten-free soy sauce
¼ cup chopped fresh basil
½ tsp sea salt
½ tsp black pepper
2 colored bell peppers, cut into 2-inch chunks
1 red onion, quarter and slice into 2-inch chunks
1 zucchini, cut into 2-inch chunks
21 large wild-caught shrimp, peeled

Directions:
Start grill or preheat oven to 400°F. Soak skewer sticks in water to prevent burning during cooking. Mix melted butter with lime juice, tamari, basil, salt, and pepper in a bowl. Toss together chopped vegetables and shrimp and coat with sauce. Allow to marinate for at least 30 minutes. Arrange veggie pieces and shrimp on a wet wooden skewer. Place directly on grill for 5-7 minutes until shrimp are cooked through and vegetables are tender, if baking, place on cookie sheet and for 12-15 minutes.

Nutrition Per Serving:
Calories 176, Total Fat 9, Carbs 6g, Protein 17g

Food as Medicine Tip: Choose wild caught shrimp only, as these will be less toxic and free of antibiotics or byproducts while being higher in the antioxidant astaxanthin and omega-3s. Astaxanthin is an antioxidant found in the pink pigmentation of marine sources that consume algae. These compounds have been shown to have high potent anti-inflammatory effects, slowing the aging process and cognitive decline.

PESTO CRUSTED
HALIBUT

PESTO CRUSTED HALIBUT

Makes:
6 Servings

Ingredients:
unbleached parchment paper
1 clove garlic, peeled
½ cup packed flat-leaf parsley
1 cup packed basil
2 Tbsp fresh thyme
2 Tbsp fresh tarragon leaves
1 Tbsp fresh oregano leaves
½ cup grated Parmesan
½ cup roasted pistachios, shelled
½ tsp sea salt
¼ tsp ground black pepper
2 Tbsp freshly squeezed lemon juice (about 2 lemons)
⅓ cup olive oil
2 pounds wild-caught halibut, cut into 4-6 oz filets

Directions:
Preheat oven to 375° F. While oven is heating, pull six 16-inch pieces of parchment paper, folding each in half and cutting a heart shape, set aside. Start food processor with "s" blade add the garlic and pulse until finely chopped. Add all of the herbs, Parmesan cheese, pistachios, salt, pepper, and lemon and blend until finely chopped. With the processor running, add the olive oil in a steady stream until the mixture becomes creamy and emulsified. Using a spatula, spread ⅛ cup of pesto on each 4-6 oz piece of halibut.

Place Halibut with pesto on parchment paper along the center of the pre-cut heart shape folding the heart in half over the fish. Starting with the top corner of the now folded heart, fold small triangles aiming for multiple 45 degree folds to seal the fish in the parchment until reaching the bottom corner, fold remaining parchment under fish to tuck in remaining paper to trap steam. Bake for 10 minutes per inch of thickness. Serve with sweet and sour vegetables or side of choice.

Nutrition Per Serving:
Calories 304, Total Fat 16g, Carbs 2g, Protein 36g

Food as Medicine Tip:
The firm while meal and delicately sweet flavor of halibut, combined with its high nutritional value, make it a favorite among fish lovers. A very good source of high quality protein, halibut are rich in significant amounts of a variety of important nutrients including the minerals selenium, magnesium, phosphorus, and potassium; the B vitamins B12, niacin, and B6; and perhaps most important, the beneficial omega-3 essential fatty acids.

ASPARAGUS PROSCIUTTO SALAD
WITH SEARED SCALLOPS

ASPARAGUS PROSCIUTTO SALAD WITH SEARED SCALLOPS

Makes:
6 Servings

Ingredients:
2 pounds asparagus, ends removed and chopped into 3 pieces
4 Tbsp butter or ghee, separated
4 oz prosciutto
¼ cup lemon juice, squeezed from 2-3 lemons
⅛ cup toasted pine nuts
½ tsp sea salt, divided
½ tsp black pepper, divided
zest of 2 lemons
12-15 large wild-caught scallops, patted dry

Directions:
Bring a pot to boil with water, toss in asparagus spears for about 3 minutes until bright green and tender. Drain immediately in sink and run under cold water. In a saute pan under medium heat, melt 2 Tbsp butter and saute asparagus pieces with prosciutto for about 3-4 minutes, stirring occasionally until starting to brown. Then remove from heat and place asparagus and prosciutto in bowl to toss with lemon juice, pine nuts, ¼ tsp salt, ¼ tsp pepper, and lemon zest. Set aside and allow flavors to combine when preparing scallops.
Heat a cast-iron pan or clean, stainless steel pan, then add remaining ghee to melt across surface. Once heated, place dry scallops sprinkled with remaining salt and pepper in single layer in pan. Allow to sit undisturbed for 3-5 minutes watching the side of the scallop to see a change in color from translucent to mildly opaque. Flip each scallop once to create a nice caramelized sear on each side, heat an additional 3 minutes.
Serve asparagus salad on plates and top with 2-3 large seared scallops. Garnish with additional zest if desired.
Note: Scallops can get rubbery if overcooked, let to sit too long, or reheated. I recommend cooking these in batches per meal for optimal results.

Nutrition Per Serving:
Calories 368, Total Fat 17g, Carbs 12g, Protein 25g

Food as Medicine Tip:
Asparagus is very high in the amino acid, Asparagine. Asparagine is synthesized from aspartate and glutamine and can be readily converted into aspartate for cellular functions including energy production. It is also a component of the urea cycle, helping to remove excess ammonia to prevent toxic overload. Asparagine can help prevent fatigue, hypothyroidism, and weight gain. Did you ever notice a certain smell to your urine after the consumption of asparagus? This is due to the fact that during digestion of Asparagus, the vegetable's sulfurous amino acids break down into smelly chemical components. And because those components are "volatile," meaning airborne, the odor wafts upward as the urine leaves the body and can be detected as soon as 15 minutes after you eat this spring delicacy.

MAPLE GLAZED
SALMON

MAPLE GLAZED SALMON

Makes:
4 Servings

Ingredients:
¼ cup grade b maple syrup
2 Tbsp tamari
2 cloves garlic, minced
¼ tsp ground black pepper
1 pound wild-caught salmon

Directions:
Mix maple syrup, soy sauce, garlic, and ground pepper in a small bowl. Cut salmon into four 2x4-inch filets at 4 oz each. Place salmon pieces in a shallow baking dish and coat with the maple syrup marinade mixture.
Cover dish and let marinate for about 30 minutes, rotating halfway through. Preheat oven to 400°F. Bake salmon for about 10 minutes per inch of thickness, until salmon is easily lifted from skin or flaked with a fork. Serve immediately as entree, but if using for a salad, let salmon rest to room temperature or to slightly warm before adding to leafy greens.

Nutrition Per Serving:
Calories 198, Total Fat 5g, Carbs 12g, Protein 24g

Food as Medicine Tip:
Why wild matters! Choosing wild caught fish is optimal as they are higher in omega-3 fatty acids and contain more protein as they have to swim against current. The diet of a wild caught fish is algae while farm-raised fish consume corn and other carbohydrates which lead to higher amount of calories with less healthy fats and less protein. Aim for sustainably caught sources, as they will have less environmental impact.

MISO GLAZED WILD SALMON
W/ GINGERY VEGETABLE STIR-FRY

MISO GLAZED WILD SALMON W/ GINGERY VEGETABLE STIR-FRY

Makes:
4 Servings

Ingredients:
20 oz wild-caught salmon, with pin bones removed and separated into 5 oz portions
1½ cups *Gingery Miso Sauce* (divided into ½ cup and 1 cup portions)
Bunch of rainbow chard
2 tsp untoasted sesame oil
1 yellow onion, chopped
2 cloves garlic, chopped
3 cups red cabbage, shredded
3 large carrots, julienned
Optional: Black sesame seeds for garnish

Directions:
Marinate wild salmon pieces in glass dish with ½ cup of *Gingery Miso Sauce* for a minimum of 45 minutes. Prepare rainbow chard by cutting away stems and setting aside leaves. Chop stems in small pieces and set aside. Chiffonade leaves of chard by rolling leaves into one hand and slicing small thin ribbons, set aside. Preheat oven to 375°F. Place salmon filets on baking sheet with skin down. Bake in oven for 10 minutes per inch of thickness.

While salmon is baking, heat large sauté pan and add sesame oil, then onions and garlic. Cook for about 3-4 minutes stirring continuously. Add chard stems, cabbage, and carrots to the pan sauté for about 4 minutes, then add ½ cup *Gingery Miso Sauce and* bring heat to a soft boil before reducing heat to a simmer for about 5 minutes. Once vegetables are slightly softened, add chard leaves and pour in remaining ½ cup sauce to braise down. Once slightly wilted, remove from heat and set aside. Plate 2 cups of vegetable stir fry with 1 salmon filet and top with sesame seeds if desired for garnish.

Nutrition Per Serving with Gingery Miso Sauce:
Calories 358, Total Fat 14g, Carbs 24g, Protein 34g

Food as Medicine Tip:
Cabbage is rich in Vitamin C and polyphenols, which protect the body from damage and inflammation. The fiber in cabbage helps sequester excess cholesterol in the bowel and lower LDL levels. Glucosinolates, the sulfur-containing compound in cabbage, inhibits cancer development and helps protect against carcinogens in the body by aiding in phase 2 detoxification. Cabbage is also a very good source of Vitamin K, which is necessary for blood clotting and bone health and B vitamins, which aid in energy production. Cabbage also contains high amounts of manganese, which promotes blood sugar balance and bone health as well as cardioprotective potassium.

COLORFUL SOBA NOODLE SALAD
WITH SEARED BUFFALO

COLORFUL SOBA NOODLE SALAD WITH SEARED BUFFALO

Makes:
6 Servings

Ingredients:
1 8 oz package soba noodles (make sure is 100% buckwheat for gluten-free)
2 Tbsp untoasted sesame oil, divided
¼ cup toasted sesame seeds
2 Tbsp toasted sesame oil
3 Tbsp tamari
1½ Tbsp balsamic vinegar
1 Tbsp grade b maple syrup
1 Tbsp hot chili pepper oil (to taste, spice preference)
¼ cup chopped cilantro leaves
2 garlic cloves, chopped
1 bunch carrots, julienned
1 bunch rainbow chard, stems removed and chopped, leaves chiffonade
2 cups snap peas
1 pound grass-fed buffalo sirloin, grilled or pan seared and oven finished*

Directions:
Cook soba noodles according to package directions. Drain and rinse in colander, toss in 2 tsp untoasted sesame seed oil to prevent sticking. To toast sesame seed, place in a dry skillet over medium heat. Keep seeds moving until they give off aroma, pop and begin to change color, about 3 minutes. Remove and set aside.
Combine dressing ingredients toasted sesame oil, tamari, vinegar, maple syrup, and hot pepper oil in small bowl; whisk together. Place drained noodles in a large bowl. Add dressing, cilantro and sesame seeds; toss gently.
Heat saute pan and add remaining untoasted sesame oil, gently sauté vegetables starting with garlic and carrots, followed by chard stems and snap peas then remove from heat and toss in chard leaves to wilt. Mix vegetables with noodles in sauce. Serve with sliced grilled buffalo sirloin slices.
*See method on pg. 134

Nutrition Per Serving:
Calories 348, Total Fat 20g, Carbs 15g , Protein 27g

Food as Medicine Tip:
This colorful dish accents Asian flavors with crunchy vegetables on a gluten-free buckwheat noodle. In stir-fry dishes, it is important to understand when to add in each vegetable. In the cooking demo, we talk about the "Root to Fruit" philosophy of introducing produce to heat. The roots such as carrots, garlic, onion, potatoes, etc. require the most cook time and typically start the dish off, followed by stems such as chard stems, asparagus, etc., followed by fruits (anything that has seeds) bell peppers, zucchini, etc. The dish is completed by tossing in leafy greens to wilt! This will help you navigate your CSA box from your local farmer and allows you to easily substitute local options in any dish when understanding how the item functions and how it needs to be treated in the cooking process.

SEARED SIRLOIN WITH
CHERRY WINE REDUCTION

SEARED SIRLOIN WITH CHERRY WINE REDUCTION

Makes:
2 Servings

Ingredients:
8-10 oz sirloin
¼ tsp cinnamon
pinch salt
¼ tsp cracked black pepper
1 Tbsp butter
½ cup *Red Wine Poached Cherry Reduction Sauce*
1 sprig thyme

Directions:
Mix together cinnamon, salt, and cracked pepper. Bring steak to room temperature and sprinkle with mixture. Heat cast-iron skillet. Once heated, add butter to pan and toss on steak. Cook for 2-4 minutes per side, per inch of thickness. Flip once only, then return to original side down and finish in oven at 450°F. Heat until internal temperature reaches 135°F for medium-rare. Allow steak to rest for about 5-8 minutes and then top with *Cherry Reduction* sauce. Cut into two pieces and garnish with a sprig of thyme.

Nutrition Per Serving:
Calories 301, Total Fat 11g, Carbs 18g, Protein 32g

Food as Medicine Tip:
Cinnamon is often paired with sweet recipes, with its most notable feature being that it can reduce blood sugar levels by increasing glucose metabolism. This reduction in glucose levels is not only beneficial for those with pre-diabetes and diabetes, but it is also beneficial for those seeking to lose weight. When our blood sugar levels are elevated, insulin levels follow. Insulin is a pro-inflammatory hormone that signals the body to store fat, so reduced insulin response is optimal.

RED WINE POACHED CHERRY REDUCTION SAUCE

RED WINE POACHED CHERRY REDUCTION SAUCE

Makes:
1 cup sauce, about 4 servings

Ingredients:
½ cup red wine (a full-bodied wine, such as a Chianti)
¼ cup balsamic vinegar
2 sprigs thyme
½ pound tart cherries, pitted (if frozen, thawed)
2 Tbsp sucanat
1 Tbsp butter
salt and cracked pepper to taste

Directions:
In a large saucepan (ideally one with meat drippings from steak) over medium-high heat, bring wine and balsamic vinegar to a low simmer along with 2 whole sprigs thyme. While the wine mixture is reducing, cut the cherries into quarters. Add the cherries and sucanat to the wine reduction; reduce heat to low, cover and cook approximately 10 minutes or until the cherries are tender. Season with salt and pepper and stir in the butter. Serve over steaks that are pan seared and oven finished.

Food as Medicine Tip:
Thyme is known to treat chest and respiratory problems including coughs, bronchitis, and chest congestion. The volatile oil components of thyme are very powerful as well including: carvacolo, borneol, geraniol,and thymol. These volatile oils of have been shown to have anti-microbial activity, helping to fight bad bacteria in the body and support the immune system!

SPAGHETTI SQUASH
CASSEROLE

SPAGHETTI SQUASH CASSEROLE

Makes:
8 Servings

Ingredients:
1 large spaghetti squash (1½-2 pounds)
½ cup water
1½ pounds ground beef
½ cup chopped onion
2 cups chopped red bell pepper, divided
3 garlic cloves, minced
2 cups canned diced tomatoes
½ tsp dried oregano
¼ tsp salt
⅛ tsp pepper
1 cup (4 oz) shredded mozzarella
1 cup (4 oz) shredded Parmesan
3 Tbsp fresh flat leaf parsley leaves, chopped

Directions:
Cut squash in half lengthwise; scoop out seeds with spoon. Place with cut side down in a baking dish; add water filling about 1-inch of the dish. Cover pan in foil and bake at 375°F for 30 minutes or until it is easily pierced with a fork. When cool enough to handle, use a fork to scoop squash out in strands.

In a skillet, cook beef until meat is browned. Drain off excess meat juices. Then add onion, 1 cup red bell pepper, and garlic; saute until softened. Add canned tomatoes, oregano, salt, and pepper to pan. Cook and stir for 3-5 minutes or until liquid is reduced. Fold in spaghetti squash to coat with meat sauce mixture. Transfer to an un-greased 9x12-inch baking dish. Top with remaining chopped bell pepper.

Bake covered, at 350°F for 25 minutes. Sprinkle with the Parmesan cheese and bake an additional 10 minutes, uncovered. Remove from oven, sprinkle with freshly chopped parsley; let stand a few minutes.

Nutrition Per Serving:
Calories 278, Total Fat 8g, Total Carbohydrate 10g, Protein 36g

Food as Medicine Tip:
Volumetrics is the focus on eating foods that are high in nutrients and volume but low in calories. These foods yield satisfaction while promoting weight loss. Cup for cup, swapping out pasta for spaghetti squash saves over 180 calories, and provides less than ⅓ of the carbohydrates. Using non-starchy vegetables, such as spaghetti squash is a great approach in applying volumetrics for optimal health outcomes!

SPICY GRASS-FED
BEEF STIR FRY

SPICY GRASS-FED BEEF STIR FRY

Makes:
4 Servings

Ingredients:
2 Tbsp olive oil
⅓ cup dry white wine
1 Tbsp grade b maple syrup
⅓ cup beef broth
2 tsp cumin
½ tsp turmeric
2 tsp chili flakes
1 hot chile pepper, seeded and chopped, about ¼ cup
4 garlic cloves, minced
1 Tbsp grated ginger
1½ pounds grass-fed flank steak, cut into strips (cut against the muscle lines)
1 yellow bell pepper, sliced
1 red bell pepper, sliced
½ pound of broccoli, cut into 1- to 2-inch pieces
½ pound snap peas, trimmed
1 bunch spinach, bottoms trimmed, roughly chopped

Directions:
Whisk together oil, wine, maple syrup, and broth. Then add cumin, turmeric, chili flakes, chopped chile pepper, garlic and ginger. Pour into glass container with steak strips and allow to marinate for at least 30 minutes.

Heat a large skillet to medium high heat. Add steak to skillet and cook 2 minutes per side or until each side is seared. Add in sliced bell pepper, broccoli, and snap peas, cook another 4-5 minutes or until steak is cooked to desired liking, and veggies are tender. Toss in spinach and simmer down with leftover steak marinade for a couple minutes ensuring marinade is thoroughly heated and begins to reduce.

Nutrition Per Serving:
Calories 358, Total Fat 18g, Carbs 15g, Protein 33g

Food as Medicine Tip:
Capsaicin is responsible for giving pepper and other spices like cayenne their heat. This compound is known for increasing thermogenesis in the body by promoting the body to burn fat for fuel. Capsaicin is also known to prevent a decline in metabolic rate that typically follows weight loss.

GARLICKY KALE STUFFED
GRASS-FED MEATLOAF

GARLICKY KALE STUFFED GRASS-FED MEATLOAF

Makes:
6 Servings

Ingredients:
2 tsp butter
1 cup chopped onion
4 cloves garlic, minced
3-4 cups fresh Lacinato or Italian kale, chiffonade leaves, discard stems
1 cup tomato paste
½ tsp pepper
½ tsp salt
1 Tbsp Dijon mustard
1.5 pounds ground beef (I recommend 90/10 blend; grass-fed)
½ cup rolled oats
2 eggs

Directions:
Heat oven 375°F. Heat butter in skillet over medium heat. Add onion, cook 6 minutes stirring frequently. Add garlic and kale, cook 1-2 minutes until wilted. Remove from heat, transfer to large bowl and let cool. Mix tomato paste, pepper, salt, and mustard in a separate bowl; set aside and let cool.

In a large bowl place ground beef, oats and eggs; mix with hands to incorporate well. Then add in tomato mixture until blended in with meat mixture. Fold in vegetables. Transfer to loaf pan and bake for 45-60 minutes based on thickness of loaf.
Monitor with meat thermometer until dish heats to 160°F internally.

Optional: If cooking sweet potatoes and asparagus at same time, start meatloaf at 375°F and at 30 minutes into baking process, turn up oven and add tray of cubed sweet potatoes. At 45 minutes into roasting, add tray of asparagus. All 3 dishes should complete around the same time, but be sure to keep an eye on each dish!

Nutrition Per Serving:
Calories 343, Total Fat 22 g, Carbs 13g, Protein 28

Food as Medicine Tip:
This dish packs a punch of nutrients from the vitamin K, folic acid, magnesium, and antioxidants of the kale, the soluble fiber from the rolled oats, as well as healthy fats, vitamin E, iron, and protein from grass-fed beef. The greens really cook down in preparation, so feel free to double the amount for a more nutrient-dense portion with greater volume and less calories. Serve with roasted asparagus and chili roasted sweet potatoes to complete the comfort food feel and balance your plate.

SLOW COOKER
CARNITAS

SLOW COOKER CARNITAS

Makes:
12 Servings

Ingredients:
1 pork shoulder or rump roast (3-4 pounds)
4 garlic cloves, thinly sliced
2 tsp pasture-raised lard
½ tsp sea salt
½ tsp ground pepper
1 bunch green onions, chopped
1½ cups minced fresh cilantro
1 cup tomatillo salsa
½ cup chicken broth
½ cup tequila or additional chicken broth
1 chopped jalapeño or 2 roasted hatch chilies
12 non-GMO organic corn tortillas (8-inch), warmed
Fresh cilantro leaves, sliced red onion and chopped tomatoes, optional

Directions:
Place roast in a 5-qt. slow cooker. Sprinkle with salt and pepper on all sides. Heat cast iron pan and put a bit of pasture-raised lard or bacon grease at the bottom. Sear all sides of roast for about 3-4 minutes per side. Return roast to slow cooker and spread oil, garlic, salt, and pepper mixture on roast. Add the onions, cilantro, salsa, broth, tequila and chilies. Cover and cook on low for 12-18 hours or until meat is tender; you should be able to pull meat off bone or shred meat simply with a fork.

Remove meat; cool slightly. Shred with two forks and return to the slow cooker; heat through. Spoon about ⅔ cup meat mixture onto each tortilla; serve with toppings of your choice such as fermented cabbage, fresh herbs, baby spinach or mixed greens, carrot shreds, beans, and/or sautéed bell peppers. Pair with a side of seasoned grilled zucchini, onions, and summer squash.

Nutrition Per Serving:
Calories 287, Total Fat 11g, Carbs 5g, Protein 42g

Food as Medicine Tip:
Lard or bacon fat can be a Healthy Choice! Lard is 45% Monounsaturated, 39% Saturated, and 11% Polyunsaturated, making it relatively stable and tolerable to moderate-high heat. Saturated fats in a quality form are a necessary aspect of a balanced diet. Saturated fat plays a role in cellular membrane health, brain function, nerve function, and can reduce your risk of heart disease....yes reduce! The addition of saturated fat to the diet reduces the levels of a substance called lipoprotein (a)—pronounced "lipoprotein little a" and abbreviated Lp(a)— that correlates strongly with risk for heart disease. Please note the emphasis on source! Buy real lard that is only a single ingredient in make-up. Pasture-raised animals are less inflammatory than those raised in confined animal feeding operations (CAFOs) that are not able to roam and are fed a diet of GMO corn/soy along with hormones and excessive antibiotics.

BOURBON PEACH
TENDERLOIN

BOURBON PEACH TENDERLOIN

Makes:
8 Servings

Ingredients:
4 ripe peaches, pitted and chopped
⅓ cup grade b maple syrup
juice of 1 lemon
3 Tbsp bourbon, optional
1 Tbsp Braggs raw apple cider vinegar
1 Tbsp Dijon mustard
1 tsp salt
¼ tsp black pepper
2 Tbsp butter or ghee
2 pounds pork tenderloin

Directions:
Preheat the oven to 375°F. Place the peaches, maple syrup and lemon juice in a small saucepan. Bring to a boil, then reduce to low heat and simmer for 15-20 minutes, stirring occasionally, until peaches begin to soften and caramelize. Add the bourbon and allow to cook down another 5 minutes.
Pour peach mixture into a blender and add the apple cider vinegar, mustard and a pinch each of salt and pepper. Blend until smooth.
Season the pork tenderloins with salt and pepper. Melt the butter over medium high heat in a large cast iron skillet, then sear the pork on all sides (2-3 minutes per side).
Pour about half of the peach glaze over the seared pork, place in the oven and bake 20-25 minutes or until internal temperature reads 145°F. Remove from the oven and allow to rest 10 minutes before slicing. Serve with additional peach glaze.

Nutrition Per Serving:
Calories 247, Total Fat 9g, Carbs 15g, Protein 25g

Food as Medicine Tip:
Pasture-raised pork is an excellent source of B vitamins and is high in anti-inflammatory, heart healthy and cancer-fighting omega 3 fatty acids as well as CLAs. Pork is also an excellent source of the amino acid tryptophan, which we usually associate with our Thanksgiving turkey, which the body uses as a precursor to serotonin. Stone fruits like peaches, plums and nectarines have been shown to ward off obesity-related diseases such as diabetes, metabolic syndrome and cardiovascular disease. They also have bioactive and phenolic compounds including quercetin and anthocyanins with anti-obesity and anti-inflammatory properties and their soluble fiber helps to reduce LDL cholesterol.

CHICKEN
PICCATA

CHICKEN PICCATA

Makes:
4 Servings

Ingredients:
4 boneless, skinless chicken breasts (about 5-6 oz each)
2 eggs
½ tsp sea salt, separated
½ cup almond flour
¼ tsp black pepper
2 Tbsp ghee
1 clove garlic, minced
⅓ cup white wine
⅓ cup *Chicken Bone Broth* (see recipe on pg. 212)
2 Tbsp capers, drained
juice of 1 lemon
2 Tbsp fresh flat leaf parsley leaves, chopped

Directions:
Lay the chicken breasts between two sheets of parchment paper and pound with a cast iron skillet until flattened, about ¼-inch thick. Beat the eggs with a pinch of sea salt in a shallow bowl. Combine the almond flour, remaining sea salt and black pepper in a separate bowl. Dip each chicken breast in the egg mixture, then coat each side with the almond flour mixture. Melt the ghee in a large cast iron skillet over medium heat. Add the chicken and cook for about 4-5 minutes per side, until it reaches an internal temperature of 165°F. Once cooked, transfer to a plate.
Add the garlic and capers to the skillet with chicken juices and browned bits and heat. Deglaze the pan with the wine and the broth, then add the lemon juice. Bring to a boil, then cook over medium heat until reduced by about half. Season to taste with salt and pepper. Add the chicken to the sauce and allow to heat through. About 2-3 minutes. Sprinkle with parsley and serve with the remaining pan sauce drizzled over a side of sautéed veggies.

Nutrition Per Serving:
Calories 374, Total Fat 20g, Carbs 3g, Protein 41g

Food as Medicine Tip:
This quick and easy chicken piccata is breaded with almond flour, which is high in monounsaturated fats and Vitamin E, making it heart healthy and anti-inflammatory. The use of ghee helps to build a delicious, rich sauce that is also high in anti-inflammatory, anti-tumorigenic and heart disease-preventing CLAs. Ghee is clarified butter, which is able to tolerate higher heat treatments as the milk solids have been removed. Along with the glutamine-rich bone broth, ghee can help to repair the gut lining and contains a compound called butyric acid that nourishes the cells of the intestines.

PESTO TURKEY MEATBALLS
AND ROASTED VEGETABLES

PESTO TURKEY MEATBALLS AND ROASTED VEGETABLES

Makes:
8 Servings

Ingredients:
1½ lbs ground white 95% lean turkey
½ lb ground dark 85% lean turkey
¾ cup finely chopped onion
4 cloves garlic, minced
1 egg
½ cup grated Parmigiano-Reggiano cheese
½ cup fresh flat leaf parsley, chopped
¼ cup fresh basil, chopped
2 Tbsp fresh oregano, chopped
2 Tbsp milk
2 tsp sea salt
1 tsp ground black pepper
1 lb fresh mozzarella, cut into small 1-inch cubes
2 Tbsp olive oil
1 jar homemade or non-processed marinara (such as Eden or Jovial brands, no added oils, no added sugar, only tomatoes and herbs)

Directions:
Preheat oven to 375 °F. Place ground turkey, onion, garlic, egg, cheese, parsley, basil, oregano, milk, salt, and black pepper in a bowl. Mix until evenly blended with hands, then form into 1½-inch meatballs. Make a hole in each meatball with your finger and place a cheese cube in the hole. Seal the meatball around the cheese and place on a nonstick baking sheet. Drizzle the oil over the meatballs. Bake until the meatballs are no longer pink in the center, about 25 minutes.
Remove pan from oven and heat the marinara sauce in a saucepan over low heat. Bring to a simmer, and place the baked meatballs in the marinara sauce for about 3-5 minutes to combine flavors. Serve with roasted vegetables or with spaghetti squash. Garnish with fresh basil.

Note: Although there is no actual pesto used in this recipe, it includes the main components of herbs, cheese, and olive oil. Consider using our pesto recipe, found in the *Sauces and Dressings* section, served over roasted vegetables if desired, in lieu of the marinara sauce.

Nutrition Per Serving:
Calories 400, Total Fat 21g, Carbs 10g, Protein 42g

Food as Medicine Tip:
During times of increased stress, our bodies use higher levels of neurotransmitters, such as serotonin. When serotonin is depleted, we can feel depressed, anxious, and our sleep can be interrupted. Turkey is very high in tryptophan, which improves serotonin production, sleep regulation and the prevention of anxiety & depression! This is why we all sleep better after eating turkey on Thanksgiving!

TARRAGON ROASTED CHICKEN
AND VEGETABLES

TARRAGON ROASTED CHICKEN AND VEGETABLES

Makes:
4 Servings

Ingredients:
16 oz boneless, skinless chicken breasts, cut into 2-inch strips
2 Tbsp balsamic vinegar
2 pints cherry or grape tomatoes
2-3 small summer squash or zucchini, chopped into 1-inch chunks
2 heads of garlic cloves, smashed and peeled
½ cup pitted Kalamata olives
2 Tbsp olive oil
Sprinkle of sea salt to taste, at least ¼ tsp
Freshly Ground pepper to taste, at least ¼ tsp
Small bunch tarragon, aim for 3 Tbsp of leaves stripped off stems

Directions:
Preheat oven to 350°F. Prep chicken by trimming fat and cutting into strips, marinate in 2 Tbsp balsamic for 3-5 minutes. Wash and prep veggies and garlic. Put olives, tomatoes, squash/zucchini, garlic in a 9x13-inch casserole dish. Pour over olive oil mixing to coat everything with the oil, sprinkle with sea salt and ground pepper.
Nestle chicken pieces into the veggie/olive mix. Strip tarragon leaves from stem, roughly chop & sprinkle over the top. Cook for about 30-35 minutes until juices from chicken, when pricked with a knife, run clear and cherry tomatoes burst.

Nutrition Per Serving:
Calories 243, Total Fat 11g, Carbs 9g, Protein 27g

Food as Medicine Tip:
Roasting is one of the best cooking methods to prepare vegetables. When we roast with a good quality oil, we are able to absorb a different spectrum of vitamins (fat soluble: A, D, E, K), and phytocompounds. The roasting process also initiates a millard effect, which is the browning or caramelizing that gives the delicious restaurant style flavor. And the fact that you can use one pan for all the vegetables is the cherry on top for quick and easy clean up!

MUSTARD
CHICKEN THIGHS

MUSTARD CHICKEN THIGHS

Makes:
4 Servings

Ingredients:
12 bone-in, skin-on chicken thighs
2 Tbsp butter, melted
2 Tbsp Dijon mustard
¼ tsp sea salt
¼ tsp ground pepper
2 Tbsp fresh tarragon
⅓ cup white wine
1 cup *Chicken Bone Broth* (see recipe on pg. 212)
¼ cup Greek yogurt
¼ cup fresh flat leaf parsley leaves, chopped

Directions:
Preheat the oven to 400°F. Place the chicken thighs skin side up in a cast iron skillet over medium high heat. Combine the melted butter, mustard, sea salt and pepper in a small bowl. Brush the mixture over the chicken thighs. Sprinkle the tarragon over the top of the chicken. Bake 35-40 minutes until a thermometer reads 165°F. Remove the chicken pieces, then place the skillet over medium heat. Deglaze with the wine, scraping any bits from the bottom. Add the bone broth and bring to a simmer to reduce the liquid by half. Once reduced, turn off heat and add the yogurt whisking continuously until a thick sauce is created. Season to taste with salt and pepper. Serve the thighs with a dollop of sauce and garnish with parsley.

Nutrition Per Serving:
Calories 419, Total Fat 27g, Carbs 2g, Protein 42g

Food as Medicine Tip:
Dark meat is often overlooked, but contains a wealth of nutrients. Dark meat delivers more iron, zinc, and selenium than white meat and is also abundant in the nutrient taurine, which can significantly lower the risk of cardiovascular disease while also protecting against diabetes and high blood pressure. It is also more satiating than white meat because of its higher calorie and saturated fat content. Bone broth is mineral rich and boosts the immune system, while improving bone and joint health as well as digestive function.

PAN SEARED CHICKEN
WITH TOMATO JAM

PAN SEARED CHICKEN WITH TOMATO JAM

Makes:
4 Servings

Ingredients:
2 Tbsp butter
4 skin-on, bone-in chicken breasts, about 1½ pounds total
½ tsp sea salt
1 tsp freshly ground black pepper
¼ cup balsamic vinegar
1 clove garlic, minced
2 pint containers cherry tomatoes, rinsed
1 bunch basil, chopped

Directions:
Preheat oven to 325°F. Heat a large cast iron skillet over high heat and add the butter. Season both sides of chicken breast with salt and pepper, to taste. Sear the chicken, bone side down for 4-5 minutes. Reduce the heat to medium, flip the chicken skin side down, cover the pan and cook on second side for 4-5 minutes.

After second side has seared, flip again so breast is skin side up. Add the balsamic, garlic, whole cherry tomatoes, and basil to skillet and place in oven for 12-15 minutes until chicken is done at 165°F. Remove chicken from skillet and let rest.
Place cast iron on burner and continue to cook until the liquid is reduced by half and cherry tomatoes "pop", mash with back of wooden spoon into a jam-like texture. Serve each chicken breast with ¼ cup of tomato mixture and a side of non-starchy vegetable of your choice.

Nutrition Per Serving:
Calories 275, Total Fat 11g, Carbs 6g Protein 38g

Food as Medicine Tip:
Basil contains a wide range of essential oils rich in phenolic compounds and a wide array of other natural products including polyphenols such as flavonoids and anthocyanins. These medicinal phytocompounds have been found to reduce inflammation and swelling and prevent aging by protecting against free radicals with its antioxidant capacity.

CURRY MANGO
CHICKEN SALAD

CURRY MANGO CHICKEN SALAD

Makes:
6 Servings

Ingredients:
1½ pounds roasted organic chicken, de-boned and chopped into ½-inch pieces
1 firm mango, diced into ¼-inch pieces
¼ cup minced scallions, green part only
4 stalks celery, diced small
½ cup Greek yogurt
1 Tbsp fresh squeezed lime juice
1 Tbsp curry powder
½ tsp ground ginger
½ tsp sea salt
6-8 butter lettuce leaves
¼ cup slivered almonds for garnish
⅓ cup chopped cilantro for garnish

Directions:
Mix first four ingredients: chicken through celery, in a medium sized bowl. Whisk yogurt, lime juice, curry, ginger, and salt in a separate small bowl. Add curry yogurt sauce to chicken mixture and stir until well coated. Serve in lettuce cups or on top of salad greens; garnish with almonds and cilantro.

Nutrition Per Serving:
Calories 210, Total Fat 9g, Carbs 8g, Protein 25g

Food as Medicine Tip:
Ginger is a well known anti-inflammatory spice that is often used as a remedy for stomach aches, as it works by relaxing or soothing the intestinal tract. Ginger is also known to have thermogenic properties that can boost your metabolism.

BROCCOLI CHICKEN DIJON

BROCCOLI CHICKEN DIJON

Makes:
4 Servings

Ingredients:
1 Tbsp butter
1-2 garlic cloves, minced
4-5 cups broccoli florets
1 pound bone-in, skin on chicken breasts (about 2 large breasts)
salt and pepper
½ cup *Chicken Bone Broth* (see recipe on pg. 212)
2 tsp low sodium tamari sauce
2 Tbsp Dijon mustard
½ cup shredded mozzarella cheese

Directions:
Preheat the oven to 375°F. Heat the butter in a large skillet over medium-high. Add the garlic and broccoli, saute stirring until crisp-tender. Remove from skillet and set aside. Season the chicken breasts with salt and pepper and place bone side down in the skillet. Sear about 4-5 minutes then flip and sear the opposite side with skin side down. Flip again so bone side is down and place in the oven to bake for 12-15 minutes, or until a meat thermometer registers 165°F.
When the chicken is done, remove from the pan and set aside, leaving the drippings in the pan. Reheat the pan over medium high heat and add the broth and tamari to the pan with drippings; mix well and bring to boil. Reduce heat to medium-low. Stir in mustard until well blended, then add the cheese a small amount at a time, whisking to incorporate for consistent texture. Return broccoli mixture to skillet; mix lightly. Remove from the heat and place chicken over the broccoli base. Pour remaining pan sauce over the chicken to serve.

Nutrition Per Serving:
Calories 330, Total Fat 16g, Carbs 13g, Protein 31g

Food as Medicine Tip:
Cruciferous vegetables are rich in detoxifying, sulfur-rich compounds. Beyond detox support, broccoli is also high in Indole-3-Carbonoles (I3Cs), which are cancer-fighting while also supporting immune and cellular function. In addition to their ability to fight against disease, I3C also aids in hormonal balance; fighting estrogen dominance by detoxing out excess estrogen, leading to reduced belly fat and fewer sleep irregularities.

Veggie Sides

Buffalo Cauliflower
Braised Greens
Roasted Balsamic Vegetables
Rosemary Roasted Yukon Gold Potatoes
Caramelized Carrots with Basil and Honey
Chili Roasted Sweet Potatoes
Simple Roasted Asparagus
Sweet and Sour Sauteed Vegetables

BUFFALO
CAULIFLOWER

BUFFALO CAULIFLOWER

Makes:
6 Servings

Ingredients:
6 cups cauliflower, cut into 1- to 2-inch pieces
2 tsp garlic powder
½ tsp sea salt
½ tsp black pepper
2 Tbsp melted ghee
½ cup hot sauce of choice
1 Tbsp butter

Directions:
Preheat oven to 425°F. Put chopped cauliflower in bowl. Mix garlic, sea salt, pepper, and melted ghee together. Coat cauliflower with ghee mixture. Roast in oven on baking sheet for 20 minutes. Mix melted butter and hot sauce in small bowl and coat roasted cauliflower. Once coated, return cauliflower to oven for another 8-10 minutes.

Nutrition Per Serving:
Calories 82, Total Fat 7g, Carbs 5g, Protein 2g

Food as Medicine Tip:
Avoid trans fats and fried foods by making your own comfort food bites at home! Trans fats have been banned from the food system, as we know they contribute towards cardiovascular disease, diabetes, and even cancer. Although partially hydrogenated oils are banned from being used in products, frying foods in low quality oil can create trans fats in the process of frying. This recipe is a great way to replace your crunchy fried cravings with the familiar flavor of wings paired with the detox supportive nutrients in the cauliflower.

BRAISED
GREENS

BRAISED GREENS

Makes:
2 Servings

Ingredients:
2 tsp ghee
½ cup *Chicken Bone Broth* (see recipe on pg. 212)
4 oz mixed greens (kale, collard, mustard, or greens of your choice); about 3-4 cups, chopped and well packed
1 clove garlic, minced
⅛ tsp sea salt
¼ tsp red pepper flakes

Directions:
Heat oil in a large skillet over medium-high heat. Add greens stirring to coat with oil. Stir until greens are barely wilted. Add garlic, salt and pepper flakes. Add bone broth to braise. Continue stirring until greens are tender, about 10-15 minutes.

Nutrition Per Serving:
Calories 70, Total Fat 7g, Carbs 0g, Protein 1g

Food as Medicine Tip:
Braising is a method of cooking in the oven. In braising, the food is cooked in liquid in a covered pan; in this case a stovetop braise. It is a combination of stewing and pot roasting. Braising vegetables will retain the maximum flavor of the ingredients while maintaining the nutritive value, unlike boiling!

ROASTED BALSAMIC
VEGETABLES

ROASTED BALSAMIC VEGETABLES

Makes:
6 Servings

Ingredients:
2 red bell peppers, seeded and cut into 2-inch chunks
1 red onion, quartered and separated into pieces
2 zucchini, cut into 2-inch chunks
2 yellow squash, cut into 2-inch chunks
1 Tbsp fresh thyme, chopped
2 Tbsp fresh oregano, chopped
2 Tbsp olive oil
2 Tbsp balsamic vinegar
½ tsp sea salt
freshly ground black pepper to taste

Directions:
Preheat oven to 375°F. In a large bowl, combine the red bell peppers, onion, zucchini, and squash. In a small bowl, whisk together thyme, oregano, olive oil, vinegar, salt, and pepper. Toss herbed balsamic mixture with vegetables until they are coated. Spread evenly on a large roasting pan or in cast-iron skillet. Roast in oven, stirring halfway through, for about 30 minutes or until vegetables are cooked through and browned.

Nutrition Per Serving:
Calories 80, Total Fat 5g, Carbs 8g, Protein 2g

Food as Medicine Tip:
Using fresh herbs is a great way to boost your intake of antioxidants and create a sophisticated flavor profile. Swapping out dried herbs for fresh herbs is a 1:3 ratio, when replacing 1 tsp of dried herbs, use 3 tsp or 1 Tbsp fresh.

ROSEMARY ROASTED
YUKON GOLD POTATOES

ROSEMARY ROASTED YUKON GOLD POTATOES

Makes:
4 Servings

Ingredients:
1 pound small Yukon gold potatoes, about 8-10
1 Tbsp grapeseed oil
1 Tbsp ghee, melted
1 tsp sea salt
½ tsp coarse ground black pepper
3 Tbsp fresh rosemary, roughly chopped

Directions:
Preheat oven to 400°F. Wash potatoes and place in baking sheet or cast iron skillet. Mix together grapeseed oil and melted ghee. Coat potatoes in oil and ghee mixture until glistening, using hands to ensure even coating. Sprinkle sea salt, pepper, and rosemary over potatoes and place in middle rack of oven to roast for about 20-25 minutes, shaking in the middle to ensure even cooking. Remove from oven when cooked through and able to smash with fork or spatula.

Nutrition Per Serving:
Calories 182, Total Fat 21g, Carbs 10g, Protein 2g

Food as Medicine Tip:
Grapeseed oil is a great alternative oil to use for high-heat dishes. The smoke point is 420°F, much higher than olive oil's 320°F. It has a light, clean taste that makes it very versatile. Use for roasting, sautéing, or baking!

CARAMELIZED CARROTS
WITH BASIL AND HONEY

CARAMELIZED CARROTS WITH BASIL AND HONEY

Makes:
4 Servings

Ingredients:
1 Tbsp coconut oil
6 medium carrots (halved lengthwise and cut into 2-inch pieces)
1 cup water (just enough to cover carrots in skillet)
2 Tbsp raw, unfiltered honey
2 Tbsp *Chicken Bone Broth* (see recipe on pg. 212)
4 Tbsp fresh basil, torn or chopped

Directions:
Heat a large skillet, add coconut oil to melt and add carrots. Sauté for 2-3 minutes then add just enough water to cover carrots. Cook over medium-high heat until water is evaporated and carrots are tender, about 10 minutes (if not evaporated at 12 minutes drain off excess water). Continue to sauté, tossing often, until carrots are light golden, about 2 minutes. Add the honey and broth. Continue to cook, stirring and scraping up browned bits with a wooden spoon, until carrots are glazed, about 2 minutes. Sprinkle in basil and serve.

Nutrition Per Serving:
Calories 98, Total Fat 4g, Carbs 18g, Protein 2g

Food as Medicine Tip:
The carrots in this recipe provide fiber, and a surplus of nutrients from their bright orange color. Carrots are rich in carotenoids. Carotenoids can help make insulin more effective, lower your risk for heart disease and help decrease your risk for cancer. Basil is a small herb but packs quite the nutritional punch, while also aiding in the body's detoxification of toxic metals! Pair this dish with seared grass-fed steak and garlic kale or use as a side.

CHILI ROASTED SWEET POTATOES

CHILI ROASTED SWEET POTATOES

Makes:
4 Servings (about ½-¾ cup each)

Ingredients:
2 sweet potatoes/yams, cut into 1-inch cubes
1-2 Tbsp coconut oil, melted
1 Tbsp chili powder
1-2 pinches cayenne (optional)
1 tsp sea salt

Directions:
Set oven to 400°F. Place cubed sweet potatoes in mixing bowl. In a separate small bowl, mix melted coconut oil with chili powder and cayenne. Pour liquid mixture over sweet potatoes and mix with hands until well coated. Lay out on cookie sheet and sprinkle with sea salt. Roast in oven for 25-30 minutes until crisp and cooked throughout.

Nutrition Per Serving:
Calories 110, Total Fat 6g, Carbs 14g, Protein 1g

Food as Medicine Tip:
This colorful root vegetable boasts an impressive nutritional profile: rich in beta-carotene (which the body then converts to Vitamin A), sweet potatoes are also good sources of Vitamin C, manganese, copper, Vitamin B6, potassium, iron, and dietary fiber. Sweet potatoes come in about 400 varieties and two main hues, with either cream- or orange-colored flesh. Anthocyanin compounds in sweet potatoes have anti-inflammatory effects, and can target brain and blood vessel health. Sweet potatoes can also aid in the release of adiponectin, a hormone in fat cells that favorably works with insulin response to balance blood sugar levels.

SIMPLE ROASTED ASPARAGUS

SIMPLE ROASTED ASPARAGUS

Makes:
4 Servings (about 8-10 spears each)

Ingredients:
2 bunches of asparagus, about 1.5 pounds
1 Tbsp ghee, melted
½ tsp sea salt
1 lemon, halved and juiced

Directions:
Set oven to 400°F. Wash asparagus and break at ends to remove woody stems or cut off last ½-inch. Lay asparagus on baking sheet and coat with melted ghee so all spears are glistening. Spread spears out so they lie in a single layer without overlap. Use two baking sheets if necessary. Sprinkle with sea salt and place in oven. Roast for 12-15 minutes, until bright green and tender. Splash with freshly squeezed lemon juice and serve.

Nutrition Per Serving:
Calories 69, Total Fat 4g, Carbs 7g, Protein 4g

Food as Medicine Tip:
Ghee is a clarified butter that has been heated to remove the lactose and casein. This also allows the fat to tolerate higher heat without oxidative damage. Ghee is a great option for roasting and is traditionally used in Indian dishes.

SWEET AND SOUR
SAUTÉED VEGETABLES

SWEET AND SOUR SAUTÉED VEGETABLES

Makes:
6 Servings

Ingredients:
1 Tbsp sesame oil
½ yellow onion, sliced
3 cups snow peas or snap peas
3 bell peppers: choose from yellow, red, orange, sliced
½ cup *Chicken Bone Broth* (see recipe on pg. 212)
3 Tbsp rice vinegar
1 Tbsp tamari
1 Tbsp raw, unfiltered honey
2 tsp arrowroot
2 Tbsp water

Directions:
Put sesame oil in heated pan. Sauté onion for 3-5 minutes, then add snow peas and peppers. While vegetables are sautéing, mix up ingredients for sauce, starting with chicken broth through honey. In another small bowl, whisk together arrowroot and water, then incorporate into the liquid sauce mixture. Pour sauce mixture over vegetables in heated pan and stir until well coated. Allow heat to work with arrowroot to thicken sauce and reduce thickness significantly, about 3-5 minutes.

Nutrition Per Serving:
Calories 76, Total Fat 2g, Carbs 11g, Protein 3g

Food as Medicine Tip:
Tamari is a wheat free soy sauce, great for Asian dishes and stir fried foods if you have celiac disease or are avoiding wheat. Coconut aminos are another great substitute for soy sauce, which is wheat AND soy free. Both tamari and coconut aminos capture the savory/umami taste that is signature in Asian foods!

Indulgences

Raw Cacao Chia Bites
Cocoa Roasted Almonds
Gingered Apple Crumble
Mango Chia Coconut Pudding
Pumpkin Chia Seed Pudding
Raw Walnut Fudge
Coconut Poached Pears
Blueberry Spinach Cobbler
Greek Yogurt Cheesecake Bars
Goat Cheese Peach Tart
Black Bean Brownies with Walnuts and Chocolate
Chunks
Banana Chocolate Ice Cream
Avocado Chocolate Mousse
Grain-Free Blueberry Pecan Cookies

RAW CACAO
CHIA BITES

RAW CACAO CHIA BITES

Makes:
16 Servings of 3 balls each

Ingredients:
1 cup whole almonds
⅔ cup pecans
½ cup walnuts
½ cup ground chia seeds
1 cup pitted dates, reserving 3-4 dates for end of recipe
1 tsp coarse sea salt
⅔ cup raw cacao powder
¼ cup grade b maple syrup
1 cup almond butter (no sugar or oil added)
2 tsp vanilla extract
½ tsp sea salt
¼ cup cacao nibs
Optional: ¼ cup coconut shreds

Directions:
Place almonds and pecans in a food processor, using standard "s" blade and pulse until chopped into pieces. Remove from processor and reserve for later in recipe. Place the walnuts and ground chia seeds in food processor and mix continuously until coarsely ground. Add the dates, and pulse until combined with the nuts. Add the coarse sea salt and pulse until well blended. Add the cacao powder, maple syrup, almond butter, vanilla, and salt. Process until the mixture is thick and smooth, gathering into a massive ball-like formation.
Add the chopped almonds, pecans, and nibs, pulse a few times until combined. You'll want the almonds to still remain in crunchy chunks. If needed, add reserved dates one at a time until mixture can be rolled into balls. Form the balls with a scoop, and then roll them between your hands to form a ball. Roll the balls in the coconut shreds if desired. Place in a sealed container in the freezer until hardened.

Nutrition Per Serving:
Calories 189, Total Fat 16g, Carbs 9g, Protein 2g

Food As Medicine Tip:
Cacao contains the highest concentration of antioxidants of any food in the world. By weight, cacao has more antioxidants than red wine, blueberries, acai, pomegranates and gogi berries combined. Dates are a good source of fiber, an excellent source of easily digested carbohydrates. Dates are among the most alkaline of foods, and contain a special type of soluble fiber called beta-D-glucan, which has been shown to decrease the body's absorption of cholesterol and balance blood sugar.

COCOA ROASTED
ALMONDS

COCOA ROASTED ALMONDS

Makes:
16 servings ¼ cup each

Ingredients:
4 cups raw organic almonds
1 large egg white
3 Tbsp raw cacao powder
1 Tbsp raw, unfiltered honey
1 tsp vanilla extract
½ tsp coarse sea salt

Directions:
Preheat oven to 350°F. Place almonds in large bowl. In a small bowl, whisk egg white until foamed and fold in cacao, honey, and vanilla. As there is variance in liquid from egg white and density of honey and cacao, add teaspoons of water, one at a time until the mixture is the viscosity of maple syrup and able to be drizzled from a spoon. Pour chocolate mixture over almonds and stir until coated. Spread on baking sheet covered with parchment paper and sprinkle with sea salt. Bake for 10-12 minutes.

*Optional: If you'd like these somewhat sweeter, add two additional teaspoons of honey to the chocolate mixture before mixing with any water. This would add an additional 1g of carbs and 3 calories to the nutrition per serving.

Nutrition Per Serving:
Calories 213, Total Fat 18g, Carbs 7g, Protein 8g

Food As Medicine Tip:
These are a great way to curb your cravings while holding over your hunger with a healthy fat. The raw dark cacao is a rich antioxidant that can improve blood sugar control and boost metabolism! These almonds have a minimal amount of carbohydrate in them from the honey, so they serve as a balanced food with a desired carbohydrate-to protein ratio.

GINGERED APPLE
CRUMBLE

GINGERED APPLE CRUMBLE

Makes:
8 servings

Ingredients:
5 apples, cored, and cut into ½-inch slices (4 cups)
1 cup rolled old fashioned oats
⅛ cup oat flour, made from pulsed rolled oats in blender
½ cup sucanat
¼ tsp sea salt
½ tsp cinnamon
2 Tbsp ginger root, peeled and finely chopped
½ cup softened butter

Directions:
Place apples in baking dish; mix oats, oat flour, sucanat, sea salt, and cinnamon in a bowl. Melt butter with ginger over stovetop, over low heat. Pour butter mixture into bowl of dry ingredients. Stir into a paste that is thick and crumbly, then crumble with hands over the apples. Bake in oven at 375°F for 45 minutes until topping is browned and apples are baked throughout.

Optional: serve with Greek yogurt to balance out carbs and add probiotics!

Nutrition Per Serving:
Calories 218, Total Fat 12g, Carbs 24g, Protein 2g

Food As Medicine Tip:
This crumble contributes just enough sweetness for a dessert, while providing soluble fiber and anti-inflammatory effects. Apples contain flavonoids, including quercetin which is anti-inflammatory, antioxidant, and anti-tumorigenic. You can use ginger juice vs. chopped ginger if you'd like. Ginger juice is made by chopping fresh peeled ginger finely and smashing the pulp between two spoons. This is a great way to add zing to soups, smoothies, and desserts without ginger's chunky texture. Cinnamon in the crumble helps to promote blood sugar regulation, prevents clumping of platelets in arteries, and provides the highest antioxidant capacity of any spice!

MANGO CHIA COCONUT
PUDDING

MANGO CHIA COCONUT PUDDING

Makes:
4 Servings

Ingredients:
1 cup full fat, canned coconut milk
1 cup filtered water
2 Tbsp raw, unfiltered honey
1 tsp vanilla extract
1 tsp cinnamon
¼ tsp ground cardamom
½ scoop *Naturally Nourished Grass-Fed Whey Protein*
pinch sea salt
⅓ cup chia seeds
1 cup mango, diced
1 Tbsp raw, unfiltered honey
berries or nuts of your choice for topping, optional

Directions:
Blend first eight ingredients (coconut milk through sea salt) until smooth.
Pour the mixture into a medium bowl and whisk in the chia seeds until thoroughly combined and mixture begins to thicken.
Refrigerate overnight or for at least three hours until thick. In the meantime, puree the mango with the tablespoon of honey until smooth. Use this mixture as a topping or layer with the pudding to create a parfait effect. Top with fresh fruit or Brazil nuts. Store in mason jars for a quick snack on the go!

Nutrition Per Serving:
Calories 277, Total Fat 15g, Carbs 27g, Protein 11g

Food As Medicine Tip:
Chia pudding makes a great snack on the go, or a quick overnight breakfast. Chia seeds are packed with anti-inflammatory omega 3 fatty acids as well as a substantial amount of fiber, making them a great addition to smoothies, breakfasts and desserts like this one. Chia seeds also help to stabilize blood sugar and create a feeling of satiety, keeping you full for longer. The addition of a scoop of the whey protein supports lean body mass and cognitive function, making this a guilt-free, health-promoting treat!

PUMPKIN CHIA SEED
PUDDING

PUMPKIN CHIA SEED PUDDING

Makes:
2 Servings

Ingredients:
½ cup unsweetened almond milk
⅓ cup pure canned or fresh pumpkin purée
4 Tbsp chia seeds
2 tsp raw, unfiltered honey
¼ tsp cinnamon
⅛ tsp nutmeg
Optional: 1 Tbsp pumpkin seeds or pecans to garnish
Optional: Cinnamon to garnish and a dollop of Greek yogurt, as pictured

Directions:
Combine almond milk, pumpkin, chia seeds, honey and spices in a bowl. Stir until well mixed. Refrigerate for at least one hour, or overnight to set. Spoon pudding into Serving glass and top with a sprinkle of cinnamon, and pumpkin seeds or cinnamon and yogurt to garnish.

Nutrition Per Serving:
Calories 194, Total Fat 9g, Carbs 20g, Protein 8g

Food As Medicine Tip:
Using fresh pumpkin and roasting it with tat is best. It steamed, be sure to add fat to absorb all of its nutritional benefits. If buying canned, look for organic, BPA-free, with no added sugar! Cinnamon aids in blood sugar balance reducing blood sugar spikes and promoting balanced insulin response. This is important, as insulin is pro-inflammatory, driving fat storage and hormonal imbalance. Also as a source of chromium, cinnamon can help to regulate cholesterol levels while providing a nice warming flavor!
Raw Unfiltered Honey contains chrysin, a natural occurring flavonoid that can trap estrogen and prevent conversion of testosterone into estrogen, through aromatization. This is found only in raw, unfiltered honey, due to the higher pollen count and crystallization.

RAW WALNUT
FUDGE

RAW WALNUT FUDGE

Makes:
12 Servings

Ingredients:
1 cup walnuts soaked in water for 2-4 hours, then strained
⅓ cup raw cacao powder
½ cup melted coconut oil
⅓ cup grade b maple syrup
2-3 Tbsp raw cacao nibs
½ tsp coarse sea salt

Directions:
Blend all ingredients (with exception of sea salt) in a food processor. Line a small pan with parchment paper and spread out mixture pressing into the pan. Sprinkle with sea salt and lightly press into the surface. Chill in freezer for at least 1 hour. Cut into pieces and store in refrigerator or freezer for up to 3 weeks, if it lasts that long!

Nutrition Per Serving:
Calories 189, Total Fat 16g, Carbs 9g, Protein 2g

Food As Medicine Tip:
Coconut oil, a medium chain fatty acid, can rev up your daily caloric burn and aid in weight loss. It also has been shown to improve the ratio of good cholesterol (HDL) to bad cholesterol (LDL). Coconut oil is rich in antioxidants and has anti-inflammatory properties. It is antifungal, antiviral, and antibacterial with the active compound Lauric acid, which is believed to fight infections. Although very healthy, it is still considered a fat, and at 120 calories per tablespoon, consume in moderation!

COCONUT POACHED
PEARS

COCONUT POACHED PEARS

Makes:
2 Servings

Ingredients:
2 tsp coconut oil
2 whole pears, sliced
1 Tbsp ginger, minced
1 tsp cinnamon, ground
⅛ tsp cardamom
¼ tsp nutmeg
⅓ cup full fat, canned coconut milk

Directions:
Heat saute pan, and add coconut oil to melt. Then add pear slices and coat with oil. Allow to simmer and soften for about 3 minutes, then add ginger, cinnamon, cardamom, and nutmeg, stirring to distribute evenly. Pour stirred coconut milk over top and allow to poach for 5 minutes. Top with 2 Tbsp freshly whisked coconut milk and a sprinkle of cinnamon to garnish.

Nutrition Per Serving:
Calories 202, Total Fat 12g, Carbs 26g, Protein 2g

Food As Medicine Tip:
This makes a great pre-bed snack! The pears are loaded with soluble fiber to hold over your appetite and the warming spices aid in lowering blood sugar levels. The MCT fat in the coconut oil and coconut milk will tonify your adrenal glands, aiding in sleep and stress regulation while boosting metabolism.

BLUEBERRY SPINACH OAT
CRUMBLE

BLUEBERRY SPINACH OAT CRUMBLE

Makes:
12 Servings

Ingredients:
½ cup butter
2 cups rolled oats
1½ cups rolled oats, pulsed in blender to oat flour
½ cup sucanat
1 tsp cinnamon
½ tsp nutmeg
¼ tsp baking powder
¼ tsp salt
1 tsp pure vanilla extract
1½ cups blueberries
1 tsp honey
1-2 tsp arrowroot
3 cups fresh spinach, packed

Directions:
Preheat the oven to 375°F. Coat an 8x8-inch baking pan with 1 tsp butter. In a large bowl, combine the oats, oat flour, sucanat, cinnamon, nutmeg, baking powder, salt, and stir to mix well.Add the vanilla and butter and cutting it quickly into the dry ingredients with two knives or forks until the mixture resembles coarse meal and is no longer powdery. Do not overmix; bits of butter will still be visible. Set aside about half of the oat mixture; press the rest of it firmly into the greased pan. Bake until lightly browned at the edges (but not fully baked) about 13-15 minutes. Meanwhile, mix blueberries with the honey in blender and pour into saucepan. Bring to a low simmer, whisking continuously and adding 1 tsp of arrowroot to the mixture, adding additional as needed to achieve a texture similar to that of fruit preserves.
Place blueberry compote back in blender. Add 3 Tbsp water to small saucepan and bring to a low boil. Add in half of the spinach leaves to steam and wilt, slowly adding more leaves until all 3 cups cook down. Add spinach mixture to the blender with blueberry blend and mix on high. Spread the blueberry mixture over the partially baked oat layer, then sprinkle with the reserved oat mixture, crumbling with fingers while distributing. Bake until the topping is slightly browned, 20-25 minutes. Remove pan from oven to cool completely before cutting into 16 bars.

Nutrition Per Serving:
Calories 174, Total Fat 8g, Carbs 20g, Protein 2g

Food As Medicine Tip:
The oats and arrowroot in this recipe provide soluble fiber to increase satiety and promote optimal blood sugar control along with reducing blood cholesterol. Arrowroot is often used as a soothing agent for painful, irritated or inflamed mucous membranes. Talk about comfort food! One of these bars is a great finishing touch and cap to a nutrient dense, well balanced meal.

GREEK YOGURT CHEESECAKE
BARS

GREEK YOGURT CHEESECAKE BARS

Makes:
16 squares

Ingredients:
5 gluten-free graham cracker sheets (20 small rectangle sections)
⅔ cup sliced almonds
¼ cup ground flax seeds
3 tablespoons unsalted butter
14 oz organic cultured cream cheese
3 Tbsp raw, unfiltered honey
¼ cup sucanat
1⅓ cups whole fat Greek yogurt
2 eggs
3 egg whites
1 pint raspberries

Directions:
Place one oven rack in middle and one in lowest position. Put a pan filled with 3-4 cups water at lowest rack to create an ideal moist environment while baking. Preheat oven to 350°F. Line bottom and two sides of an 8x8-inch glass baking dish with one sheet of unbleached parchment paper, leaving a 2-inch overhang on both sides. Repeat with a second sheet of parchment, crisscrossing the first, again leaving a 2-inch overhang on sides. This is helpful to lift out the end product to slice outside of pan.
Finely grind graham crackers, flax seeds and almonds in a food processor with "s" blade. Add butter and process until mixture forms moist crumbs. Press mixture into the bottom of parchment lined pan. Chill until ready to use. Combine cream cheese, honey, and sucanat in a large food-processor with "s" blade and process until smooth and creamy. Beat in yogurt. Beat in eggs and egg whites one at a time, until well blended. Pour batter over crust.
Place cheesecake on middle rack and bake, undisturbed (don't peek at it by opening oven), until set in center, 45–55 minutes, being careful not to brown top. Cheesecake will still jiggle in the middle but will set as it cools. Remove from oven and let cool to room temperature, then cool further in fridge covered. Using parchment overhangs, remove cheesecake from pan and transfer to a counter top. Cut into 2x2-inch squares, being careful not to cut through paper. Carefully lift each square away from paper and transfer to a serving platter. Top each square with 3-4 berries.

Nutrition Per Serving:
Calories 185, Total Fat 13g, Carbs 11g, Protein 7g

Food As Medicine Tip:
Cheesecake for breakfast? it can be done and it can be guiltless! Indulge in this balanced treat filled with antioxidants, fiber, heart healthy fats, and protein to aid in brain function and lean body mass. This can be a mindful indulgence as a dessert or truly can serve as a balanced start to the day!

GOAT CHEESE PEACH
TART

GOAT CHEESE PEACH TART

Makes:
8 Servings

Ingredients:
For the crust:
1 cup almond flour
1 cup hazelnut flour
2 Tbsp butter
1 egg
pinch sea salt
For the filling:
4 oz goat cheese
½ cup Greek Yogurt
1 egg
¼ cup raw, unfiltered honey
1 tsp vanilla extract
For the topping:
3-4 ripe peaches
juice of 1 lemon
raw, unfiltered honey

Directions:
Preheat the oven to 350°F. Combine all of the crust ingredients in the food processor until dough begins to form a ball. Press the dough into an 8-inch pie pan greased with grassfed butter. Bake for 8-12 minutes, until lightly browned. Keep a close eye on the crust, as you will bake again with the filling and do not want it to get too dark! Remove from the oven and allow to cool completely. In the meantime, make the filling. Process the filling ingredients in the food processor until smooth. Pour the filling into the cooled crust. Place on a baking sheet surrounded by 1-inch of water. This will keep the filling from cracking while it bakes. Bake 20-25 minutes, until the filling it set and no longer jiggly in the center. Allow to cool completely. While the tart bakes, slice the peaches thinly and sprinkle with the lemon juice. When ready to assemble, overlap the peaches starting from the outside of the tart and working inwards in concentric circles. Top with a drizzle of raw honey and optional blueberries, blackberries or raspberries.

Nutrition Per Serving:
Calories 311, Total Fat, 23g, Carbs 18g, Protein 12g

Food As Medicine Tip:
Stone fruits like peaches, plums and nectarines have been shown to ward off obesity-related diseases such as diabetes, metabolic syndrome and cardiovascular disease. They also have bioactive and phenolic compounds including quercetin and anthocyanins with anti-obesity and anti-inflammatory properties and their soluble fiber helps to reduce LDL cholesterol. The combination of goat cheese and Greek Yogurt makes for a protein-rich, tangy tart filling that is loaded with protein as well as beneficial K2, which helps to prevent calcification of the arteries and decreases the risk of cardiovascular disease and osteoporosis.

BLACK BEAN BROWNIES WITH WALNUTS
AND CHOCOLATE CHUNKS

BLACK BEAN BROWNIES WITH WALNUTS AND CHOCOLATE CHUNKS

Makes:
12 Servings

Ingredients:
1 15.5 oz can black beans, rinsed and drained
3 eggs
3 Tbsp coconut oil, melted (plus a tsp for greasing)
¼ cup raw cacao powder
¼ tsp sea salt
1 tsp vanilla extract
¾ cup sucanat
2 oz dark chocolate bar, soy-free, organic, at least 80% cacao
¼ cup walnuts, chopped

Directions:
Preheat oven to 350°F. Lightly grease an 8x8-inch square baking dish with coconut oil. Combine the black beans, eggs, oil, cacao powder, salt, vanilla extract, and sucanat in a blender; blend until smooth; pour the mixture into the prepared baking dish. Break up chocolate bar into tiny pieces about ¼ of an inch. Sprinkle the chocolate pieces and walnuts over the top of the mixture. Bake in the preheated oven until the top is dry and the edges start to pull away from the sides of the pan, about 30 minutes.

Nutrition Per Serving:
Calories 156, Total Fat 8g, Carbs 9g, Protein 3g,

Food As Medicine Tip:
Suca-WHAT? Sucanat is a sugar extracted from sugar cane prior to the removal of molasses. Sucanat is significantly less processed than table sugar and provides your body with B vitamins, minerals, and nutrients that aid in regulating cravings and reducing stress levels!

BANANA CHOCOLATE
"ICE CREAM"

BANANA CHOCOLATE "ICE CREAM"

Makes:
6 Servings

Ingredients:
¼ cup unsweetened almond milk
3 bananas, peeled and sliced into rounds and then frozen
2 Tbsp unsweetened raw cacao powder (must be unsweetened and raw for optimal antioxidants and nutrients)
1 scoop *Naturally Nourished Grass-fed Whey Protein*
Pinch of sea salt
Optional: chopped walnuts

Directions:
Blend ingredients in food processor with "S" blade until light and fluffy. Top with chopped walnuts if desired!

Nutrition Per Serving:
Calories 189, Total Fat 16g, Carbs 9g, Protein 2g

Food As Medicine Tip:
This recipe offers a mix of antioxidant rich compounds from raw cacao, which aid in elevating mood, lowering blood pressure, and prevention of aging. Adding grass-fed protein powder curbs the glycemic index of the carbohydrates from the banana. Although this recipe provides a satisfaction for your sweet tooth, it should not raise blood sugar levels dramatically and the nutrients in a frozen banana are superior to that of a processed or refined sugar.

AVOCADO CHOCOLATE MOUSSE

Makes:
6 Servings

Ingredients:
2 avocados
½ cup pitted dates (preferably Medjool)
3-4 Tbsp cacao powder
1-2 Tbsp vanilla
pinch of Sea salt

Directions:
Blend all ingredients in a food processor. Scrape the sides with a spatula and continue to blend until smooth. Lightly sprinkle with sea salt and serve with fresh fruit.

Note: use this mousse as a dip for fresh fruit to still get the benefits of the healthy fats of the avocado with fewer calories!

Nutrition Per Serving:
Calories 156, Total Fat 11g, Carbs 13g Protein 3g

Food As Medicine Tip:
Avocados are higher in potassium than bananas. They also offer a great source of vitamin E, K, B6, and folate. They have a healthy fatty acid profile that has demonstrated through research to protect against prostate and breast cancer, as well as heart disease. When selecting a cocoa powder to use, pick one with at least 70% Cacao. Cacao is the natural cocoa bean and healthy aspect that chocolate is made from. Cacao has a high antioxidant capacity exceeding red wine, green tea, and other exotic superfoods. Cacao is very high in magnesium, which can help to lower blood pressure levels and relax muscles.

GRAIN-FREE BLUEBERRY PECAN
COOKIES

GRAIN-FREE BLUEBERRY PECAN COOKIES

Makes:
16 Servings, 1 cookie each

Ingredients:
1 cup almond meal (almond flour)
¼ cup hazelnut flour
½ cup unsweetened coconut, shredded
½ tsp baking powder
¼ tsp sea salt
¼ cup sucanat
1 egg
1 Tbsp grade b maple syrup
2 Tbsp plus 1 tsp coconut oil, melted
1 tsp vanilla extract
1 Tbsp cashew butter, softened
¼ cup dried blueberries
¼ cup pecans, chopped

Directions:
In a large mixing bowl, stir together almond meal, hazelnut flour, coconut, baking powder, sea salt, and sucanat. In a separate bowl, beat egg until uniform in color and doubled in volume. In egg bowl, whisk in the maple syrup, coconut oil and vanilla, then add cashew butter and mix until maple syrup viscosity is achieved adding teaspoons of water as needed to thin out (the variance will be on how liquid or firm the cashew butter is). Add the wet mixture to dry ingredients, and mix until just combined. Then stir in blueberries and pecans to incorporate. Chill in the fridge for at least 2 hours or overnight. Preheat oven to 375°F. Shape dough into 1-inch balls, place on ungreased baking sheet with 1½-inch space in between each. Using your palm, press down to flatten to about a ½-inch thick. Bake until edges begin to brown, 7-10 minutes. Remove from oven and let cool before serving.

Nutrition Per Serving:
Calories 110, Total Fat 8g, Carbs 9g Protein 2g

Food as Medicine Tip:
Vanilla has been used for centuries as an antioxidant and cognitive enhancing agent, to calm stomach pains, reduce hunger pangs, and relieve stress. Vanilla contains chemicals called vanilloids that activate receptors in a similar way to capsaicin, which is well known to reduce inflammation and improve mental performance. Vanilla is an aromatic stimulant, with a tendency towards the nervous system. Beyond baking, the use of vanilla essential oils are another way to increase concentration and calm the mind!

Therapeutic Foods

Chicken Bone Broth
Grass-Fed Beef Knuckle Broth
Bone Broth 3-Ways
Coconut Ginger Peach Gelatin
Cranberry Gelatin
Ginger Zinger Matcha Whip
Water Infusions

CHICKEN BONE BROTH

CHICKEN BONE BROTH

Makes:
16, 8 oz Servings

Ingredients:
1 whole, raw chicken
1.5 Tbsp ghee or butter
1 Isp sea salt (+ more to taste)
2 tsp black pepper
1 yellow onion with skin, quartered and then chopped in half
3 carrots, chopped in 2- to 3-inch pieces
4-5 ribs celery, keep leaves on, chopped
3-4 cloves garlic, skinned, smashed
1-3 cups vegetable scraps (onion skins, chard stems, carrot tops, etc.)
2 Tbsp Braggs raw apple cider vinegar
2 Tbsp turmeric, ground or fresh and chopped
2-3 bay leaves
filtered water to fill stock pot

Directions:
Coat inside (cavity) and outside of chicken with ghee, sea salt, and black pepper. Roast chicken in oven at 350°F for 1½ Hours, until the juices run clear. Remove skin, discard. Remove and reserve meat for chicken salad, soup (or eat for dinner). Put the carcass into 4-quart pot or slow cooker and pour in liquid from roasting pan. Cut the onions, carrots and celery into a few large pieces and add to the pot (slow cooker). Cover all bones and veggies with water and put on stove. Bring the pot to a boil, and then reduce heat to a slow simmer. Note if using slow cooker, run on high for first 4 hours. Add vinegar, turmeric, sea salt, and bay leaves. Let it simmer with top on until bones are soft and broth is a rich yellow hue, at least 24 hours but up to 36 hours is great! Do not agitate or stir broth once cooking to allow optimal collagen formation in broth, allowing it to gel. If looking to make a more concentraated stock, remove lid for last 4-6 hours to condense liquid. Then cool slightly and strain the stock into a freezer-safe container. Be sure to leave 1-2 inches room, for expansion as it freezes if glass; if plastic, cool completely in fridge, in glass first. Discard bones and vegetables. Option: You may also use a pre-roasted rotisserie chicken. Debone and discard skin, reserve meat for chicken salad or soup and then begin recipe from first step above with the carcass.

Nutrition Per Serving:
Calories 40, Total Fat 3g, Carbs 0g, Protein 3g

Food as Medicine Tip:
Chicken Soup has long been promoted as a "cure" for the common cold and University of Nebraska researchers validated this claim when they found a favorable white blood cell and immune response following consumption. Cold symptoms result from an accumulation of white blood cells in the bronchial tubes, so the ability to block the build up reduces symptoms or advancement of illness. In fact, the amino acid cysteine, released from chicken during cooking, chemically resembles the bronchitis drug acetylcysteine. N-Acetyl Cysteine found in bone broth supports the body's detox process and the building of glutathione, the most potent anxtioxidant in the human body! Use sea salt to create a nice salty broth which keeps mucus thin the same way cough medicines do. Give your soup a boost with garlic, onions, carrots, and celery, which can increase your soup's immune-boosting power.

GRASS-FED BEEF
KNUCKLE BROTH

GRASS-FED BEEF KNUCKLE BROTH

Makes:
16, 8 oz Servings

Ingredients:
5-8 lbs beef knuckle bones
A freezer bag full of vegetable scraps (carrot peelings, onion tops, celery leaves etc. Don't use brassicas or beets as they contribute an off-taste to the beef stock.)
filtered water to fill stock pot
2 Tbsp Braggs raw apple cider vinegar
2-3 bay leaves

Directions:
Rinse and clean the bones under filtered water. Pat them dry. Roast the bones at 400°F for about an hour until the bones are well-browned and fragrant. Roasting the bones ensures a good flavor in the resulting beef stock. Failure to do so may lend a sour or off-taste to the end product. Once the bones are browned, drain off any fat. Add the bones to a big pot or slow cooker along with any vegetable scraps you might have. Add filtered water to cover and bring to a boil. Once you've brought the water to a boil, add the vinegar and bay leafs. Turn down the heat and continue to simmer for at least 24 hours, upwards of 48. When the stock is finished simmering, filter through a fine mesh sieve and bottle in mason jars. The stock should set just like gelatin, and the fat should rise to the top. Pick off the fat and reserve it for cooking, then scoop out the gelled stock and reheat to serve as soup or broth in any cooking dish or to sip on 6 oz daily. The fat at ⅛-inch or more can preserve the broth in the fridge for upwards of 3 months; alternatively freeze.

Nutrition Per Serving:
Calories 80, Total Fat 7g, Carbs 0g, Protein 5g

Food as Medicine Tip:
Bone broth has another star amino acid, glutamine, which aids in rebuilding the gut where most of the immune system is regulated. Bone broth is like a "facelift" for the gut as the glutamine sealant is paired with collagen, which tightens gut junctions to aid in repair from "leaky gut" while supporting improved ability to absorb nutrients.

BONE BROTH
3-WAYS

BONE BROTH 3-WAYS

Whether you are having chicken or beef bone broth, these combinations can add nourishment in the form of anti-inflammatory compounds, probiotics, protein, and sulfur compounds to aid in detox processes! Dressing up your bone broth aids in making it a nourishing snack and can even be doubled to create a meal in a cup! Each recipe starts with 1-2 cups of bone broth, then add the topping combinations below.

Miso + Wild Cod + Sesame

Ingredients:
2 cups bone broth of choice
4-6 oz wild cod, cut into 1-inch cubes
2 Tbsp miso
2 Tbsp scallions
1 Tbsp sesame seeds

Directions:
When heating broth over the stove, add wild cod to cook in a simmer until cooked through; about 4-5 minutes. Remove from heat and stir in miso, scallions, and sesame seeds.

Emulsified Ghee + Turmeric

Ingredients:
1 cup bone broth of choice
1 Tbsp turmeric powder
1 Tbsp ghee
1 tsp coconut oil

Directions:
Heat up bone broth over the stove and then turn off heat. Add broth and remaining ingredients to blender. Emulsify this combo with your broth in a blender on high for at least 90 seconds.

Herbs and Carrots

Ingredients:
1 cup bone broth of choice
2 Tbsp chopped herbs of choice: basil, parsley, mint, oregano, scallions
Optional: celery, carrots, rotisserie chicken

Directions:
Heat up bone broth over the stove and add optional celery and carrots. Remove from heat to add fresh herbs, choosing 2-3 options tops. Optional: top with 2-4 oz shredded chicken.

COCONUT GINGER
PEACH GELATIN

COCONUT GINGER PEACH GELATIN

Makes:
8 servings

Ingredients:
½ cup boiling water
2 medium size peaches, pitted and sliced
½ cup full fat, canned coconut milk
1-inch ginger root, peeled
½ cup gelatin

Directions:
Heat water in saucepan to a boil. While water is heating, blend peaches, coconut milk and ginger until well combined. This should become 2 cups total of volume; add more peaches if needed. Pour peach mixture into boiling water and add gelatin. Whisk to blend ingredients; at first it will be thick and chunky. While continuously whisking, bring mixture to a simmer, then lower heat and continue whisking until mixture thins and becomes smooth. Pour into 9x9-inch pyrex or molds and set in refrigerator for at least 1 hour.

Nutrition Per Serving:
Calories 66, Total Fat 7g, Carbs 5g, Protein 1g

Food as Medicine Tip: Tip:
Combining peaches and ginger with gelatin creates a synergy of anti-inflammatory effects. The coconut milk helps to support the immune system with its lauric acid, antimicrobial lipids and capric acid, which have antibacterial, antifungal and antiviral properties. The body converts lauric acid into monolaurin, which helps fight viruses and bacteria. The gelatin helps repair "leaky gut" and improves digestion by acting like a "sealant on the tank". The combination of these ingredients to make a jello-like dessert is powerful and delicious!

CRANBERRY
GELATIN

CRANBERRY GELATIN

Makes:
10 Servings

Ingredients:
½ cup water
1½ cups 100% cranberry juice, tart unsweetened
juice of ½ lime
½ cup gelatin

Directions:
Place water, cranberry, and lime juice in saucepan and bring to a boil. Bring down to a simmer and add in gelatin powder, stirring to combine. Continue to whisk for about 60 seconds until smooth and texture has thinned. Pour into 9x9-inch pyrex or molds and set in refrigerator for at least 1 hour.

Nutrition Per Serving:
Calories 43, Total Fat 0g, Carbs 2g, Protein 10g

Food as Medicine Tip:
Gelatin is largely composed of the amino acids glycine and proline which are found in the bones, fibrous tissues and organs of animals. These amino acids are needed not only for proper skin, hair and nail growth, but also for optimal immune function and weight regulation. Cooking collagen turns it into gelatin, which can help to heal intestinal permeability or "leaky gut"!

GINGER ZINGER
MATCHA WHIP

GINGER ZINGER MATCHA WHIP

Makes:
1 serving

Ingredients:
1-inch ginger root, sliced thinly
1-inch turmeric root, sliced thinly
1 tsp matcha organic green tea powder
12 oz water
2 tsp raw coconut oil
1 tsp butter

Directions:
Steep ginger and turmeric in hot water for 7-10 minutes, then strain off ginger and turmeric slices, leaving liquid mixture for recipe base. Using a blender or emulsifier, whip in matcha. Once incorporated, whip in coconut oil (in solid form, refrigerate if necessary) and butter for 30-60 seconds until a frothy head is formed.
Optional: top with cinnamon

Nutrition Per Serving:
124 Calories, Total Fat 15 g, Carbs 0g, Protein 0g

Food as Medicine Tip:
As an option that supports intermittent fasting, this recipe features all the benefits of starting your day with pure concentrated fats, combining medium chain triglycerides (MCT) oils from coconut oil and conjugated linoleic acids (CLA) from grass-fed butter to boost metabolism and fat burn on the body while sustaining the release of caffeine into the bloodstream. This unique combo of ingredients is accented with anti-inflammatory support of ginger, and turmeric while delivering L-theanine from matcha which functions as a pilot in your brain, aiding in balancing neurotransmitters and stress-related compounds.

WATER
INFUSIONS

WATER INFUSIONS

Makes:
1 serving

Directions:
Just drop a few slices of your chosen fruit, along with a few sprigs of herbs in your stainless steel or glass container and fill with 32 to 40 fl oz filtered water.

Note: you can even cut up individual servings ahead of time and make freezer packs to pop in your water on the go!

Ideas to jazz up your water:
Strawberry and Basil
Cucumber and Mint
Lemon and Rosemary
Orange and Ginger
Blackberry and Lime
Citrus and Cilantro
Grapefruit and Thyme
Pineapple and Sage
Kiwi and Strawberry
Watermelon and Mint
Raspberry and Lime
Honeydew Melon and Mint
Ginger and Pear

Food as Medicine Tip::
The human body is made up of more than 60% water, and our muscles and brain are over 75%. Water functions to regulate body temperature, enhance metabolism and aids in detoxification as well as the absorption and transport of nutrients in the body. Water and tea infusions are an excellent way to improve the taste of your water, and they also add additional nutrients and antioxidants. Adding a solute to water also increases your body's ability to absorb the fluid into your cells and maintain electrolyte balance. Aim for at least half your bodyweight each day in fluid ounces of water to maintain optimal hydration!

Dressings and Sauces

Pumpkin Seed Pesto
Gingery Miso Sauce
Zingy Ginger Dressing
Rustic Balsamic Dressing
Simple Balsamic Vinaigrette
Blueberry Vinaigrette
Tahini-Lemon Dressing
Bright Minty Pepper Dressing & Marinade
Zesty Citrus Dressing

PUMPKIN SEED
PESTO

PUMPKIN SEED PESTO

Makes:
2 cups, as eight ¼ cup servings

Ingredients:
1½ cups raw pumpkin seeds
¼ tsp sea salt
2 Tbsp lemon juice, or to taste
3 cloves garlic
1 cup roughly chopped fresh basil
¼ cup roughly chopped mint
¼ cup olive oil
¼ cup filtered water, as needed

Directions:
Toast the pumpkin seeds, dry, in a medium sized skillet at medium heat until fragrant and puffed, moving frequently so as not to burn. Allow to cool.

Place the pumpkin seeds in a food processor and pulse until coarsely ground. Add the salt, lemon juice, garlic and herbs and pulse until roughly combined. With the food processor running, stream in the olive oil and pulse to desired consistency, adding water to thin, as needed, one tablespoon at a time.

Nutrition Per Serving:
Calories 161, Total Fat 13g, Carbs 4g, Protein 7g

Food as Medicine Tip:
Pumpkin seeds are a great source of zinc and essential fats to promote healthy testosterone levels and balanced estrogen in the body. When adding an acid to a mineral rich food, such as lemon juice with vitamin C and other limonene antioxidants, it increases the absorption of minerals available in the dish. Basil serves as an aphrodisiac, rich in vitamin A, magnesium, potassium, and vitamin C with libido lifting history dating back to ancient Greece.

GINGERY MISO
SAUCE

GINGERY MISO SAUCE

Makes:
23 Servings, 2 Tbsp each

Ingredients:
¼ cup organic miso
1 Tbsp toasted sesame oil
1 Tbsp fresh grated ginger
2 Tbsp fresh garlic, chopped
¼ cup Braggs raw apple cider vinegar
1¼ cups *Chicken Bone Broth*; add ¼ cup at a time (see recipe on pg. 212)
1½ Tbsp arrowroot

Directions:
Combine miso, oil, ginger, and garlic in large saucepan over medium heat; stir continuously until well blended. Add vinegar and ¼ cup broth, mix well and bring to a boil. Once mixture begins to boil, immediately reduce to low heat and simmer, stirring constantly. Add remaining broth slowly until blended, reserving a ¼ cup. Once well combined, in a separate bowl mix remaining ¼ cup broth with arrowroot to make a slurry; add to saucepan and stir continuously. Increase heat, bringing mixture to a soft boil, stir about every 15-30 seconds to thicken into a sauce with maple syrup like viscosity. Store in refrigerator for 8-10 days.

Nutrition Per Serving:
Calories 33, Total Fat 2g, Carbs 3g, Protein 0g

Food as Medicine Tip:
The whole soy truth! I am not a huge fan of soy in general, due to its phytoestrogen activity (plant based estrogen mimicking) and pro-inflammatory omega-6s. However, it does have some valuable plant compounds, including genistein which functions as an antioxidant, reducing inflammation and fighting against tumor activity as an anti-angiogenesis compound. Although it does have estrogen-like properties, it typically binds to the receptor, less correlated to estrogen-related cancer risk or estrogen dominance. It also provides a great source of plant sterols which can reduce LDL cholesterol levels in the body. Eating soy in moderation is a balanced approach to optimal eating. Select options that are in a whole food form and are sprouted or fermented to decrease the anti-nutrient activity of the legume. Tempeh (fermented soy loaf), Miso (fermented soy paste), and Natto are among my favorite options. I recommend avoiding soy protein isolate seen in many processed foods and soy milk as it is highly refined and all too often is genetically modified.

ZINGY GINGER
DRESSING

ZINGY GINGER DRESSING

Makes:
10 Servings, 2 Tbsp each

Ingredients:
½ cup Braggs raw apple cider vinegar
¼ cup filtered water
2 Tbsp raw, unfiltered honey
1-inch ginger root
Pinch sea salt
½ cup olive oil

Directions:
Blend ingredients (except oil) in blender. Once mixed, pour in oil as blender is running to emulsify. Serve with maple glazed salmon and raw salad greens! Add pear and walnuts or roasted pecans, goat cheese, pickled onions, etc. Store in a cool, dark place for 7-10 days.

Nutrition Per Servings:
Calories 90, Total Fat 9g, Carbs 3g, Protein 0g

Food as Medicine Tip:
Why salad dressing is essential! It is important to include fat and acid with leafy greens to absorb all their nutrients. Olive oil is a great choice for your fats and acids can come from vinegar or citrus. Store bought dressings will be loaded with binders, fillers, and GMO or pro-inflammatory fats such as soybean or cottonseed oil.

RUSTIC BALSAMIC
VINAIGRETTE

RUSTIC BALSAMIC VINAIGRETTE

Makes:
8 Servings, 2 Tbsp each

Ingredients:
½ cup balsamic vinegar
½ cup cold-pressed olive oil
1 tsp Djjon mustard
1 Tbsp organic grade b maple syrup
4 Tbsp chopped fresh rosemary
2 Tbsp chopped fresh basil
Pinch of sea salt
Pinch of black pepper, ground

Directions:
Mix vinaigrette ingredients in jar with lid and shake vigorously for 1 minute to emulsify and combine well. Store at room temperature in cool, dark place for 7-10 days.

Nutrition Per Serving:
Calories 177, Total Fat 17g, Carbs 7g, Protein 3g

Food as Medicine Tip:
Rosemary contains substances that are useful for stimulating the immune system, lowering inflammation, increasing circulation, and improving digestion. Rosemary has also been shown to increase the blood flow to the head and brain, improving concentration. So next time you have to take an exam or have a presentation at work, bring some rosemary to smell!

SIMPLE BALSAMIC
VINAIGRETTE

SIMPLE BALSAMIC VINAIGRETTE

Makes:
4 Servings, 2 Tbsp each

Ingredients:
¼ cup balsamic vinegar
1 tsp organic, grade b maple syrup
2 tsp Dijon mustard
pinch sea salt
½ tsp black pepper, to taste
¼ cup cold-pressed olive oil or walnut oil

Directions:
Combine balsamic through black pepper, while agitating or whisking pour in olive oil or shake vigorously. Store in a cool, dry place for 7-10 days.

Nutrition Per Serving:
Calories 141, Total Fat 14g, Carbs 4g, Protein 0g

Food as Medicine Tip:
Grade B maple syrup is a better choice than Grade A! Maple syrup is graded solely by its color. As the weather warms up, the sap coming from the trees becomes darker in color, producing a darker syrup with richer mineral content and stronger flavor. The State of Vermont distinguishes four maple syrup grades. From light to dark they are: Fancy, Grade A Medium Amber, Grade A Dark Amber, and Grade B.

BLUEBERRY
VINAIGRETTE

BLUEBERRY VINAIGRETTE

Makes:
6 Servings, 2 Tbsp each

Ingredients:
⅛ cup blueberries
¼ cup balsamic vinegar
1 tsp grade b maple syrup
2 tsp Dijon mustard
pinch sea salt
½ tsp black pepper, to taste
¼ cup cold-pressed olive oil or walnut oil

Directions:
To make the dressing, ingredients blueberries through black pepper to blender. Once mixed, add oil of choice while blender is going to emulsify. Store in refrigerator for 5-7 days.

Nutrition Per Serving:
Calories 143, Total Fat 14g, Carbs 5g, Protein 0g

Food as Medicine Tip:
Mustard is part of the cruciferous family of vegetables, known to have detoxifying and anti inflammatory properties. Mustard seeds have also been known to speed metabolism by up to 25%!

TAHINI-LEMON
DRESSING

TAHINI-LEMON DRESSING

Makes:
12 Servings, 2 Tbsp each

Ingredients:
¾ cup tahini
5 Tbsp fresh lemon juice
2 small garlic cloves, minced
¾ -1½ cups filtered water (based on desired thickness)
½ tsp sea salt, to taste
Handful of fresh flatleaf parsley leaves, finely minced
Pinch cayenne pepper, to taste

Directions:
Place tahini, lemon juice, and garlic in blender. Once mixed, begin pouring in water with motor running, checking to monitor consistency. Add more water for salad dressing, less water for a dip. Once it reaches desired thickness, remove from blender and stir in salt, parsley, and cayenne to taste. Store in refrigerator for 5-7 days.

Nutrition Per Serving:
Calories 121, Total Fat 7g, Carbs 7g, Protein 2g

Food as Medicine Tip:
Tahini is rich in minerals such as phosphorus, lecithin, magnesium, potassium, and iron. It's a good source of Methionine, which aids in liver detoxification. Tahini is also one of the best sources of calcium! Tahini helps to promote healthy cell growth, and can help to prevent anemia.

BRIGHT MINTY PEPPER DRESSING
& MARINADE

BRIGHT MINTY PEPPER DRESSING & MARINADE

Makes:
12 Servings, 2 Tbsp each

Ingredients:
½ cup packed fresh spearmint leaves
½ cup freshly squeezed lemon juice (2 lemons)
4-5 garlic cloves, peeled
2 Tbsp shallot
1 tsp whole black peppercorns
1 tsp sea salt
⅔ cup extra virgin olive oil

Directions:
Add all ingredients except for olive oil to a blender. Blend on high until very smooth, 1-2 minutes. Add the olive oil while continuing to blend on low speed until just incorporated. Pour into a glass jar and store in the refrigerator for 8-10 days. Bring to room temp before serving.

Note: This can also be used as a marinade for chicken or lamb for 1 hour prior to grilling, searing, or roasting.

Nutrition Per Serving:
Calories 108, Total Fat 12g, Carbs 1g , Protein 0g

Food as Medicine Tip:
A chemical compound in peppercorns called piperine may be able to help prevent a breast cancer tumor from developing, according to a study done by the University of Michigan. When eating with turmeric, black pepper enhances bioavailability of the turmeric. Sneak some turmeric into your dishes whenever cooking with pepper for an extra Food as Medicine Boost!

ZESTY CITRUS
DRESSING

ZESTY CITRUS DRESSING

Makes:
4 Servings, 2 Tbsp each

Ingredients:
juice of 1 orange; about 3 Tbsp fresh orange juice
juice of 1 lime; about 1 Tbsp fresh lime juice
2 tsp raw, unfiltered honey
½ tsp sea salt
1 Tbsp rice vinegar
¼ cup extra virgin olive oil

Directions:
Whisk together citrus, honey, sea salt, and vinegar. Once combined, continue whisking and slowly pour in olive oil to emulsify and create creamy texture. Store in refrigerator for 8-10 days.

Nutrition Per Serving:
Calories 146, Total Fat 14g, Carbs 7g, Protein 0g

Food as Medicine Tip:
Sea Salt contains many essential trace minerals that your body needs in order to be healthy and is a better choice than iodized salt. Sea salt contains the natural electrolyte, potassium which is essential for helping muscles function properly. Sea salt also helps the body to absorb the potassium better from other foods, making it effective in helping to prevent muscle pains, spasms and cramps.

INDEX

All recipes in this book are gluten-free, antioxidant-rich, and anti-inflammatory. Below is a layout of categories to aid in selection of options that limit additional ingredients.

Please Note: This book is limited in recipes containing soy due to its proinflammatory and goitrogenic effects. If a recipe has soy it would be in the form of tamari or miso which offer therapeutic effects. Tamari can be replaced in equal parts with coconut aminos for those strictly avoiding soy.

GF grain-free
EF egg-free
DF dairy-free
KF ketosis-friendly

SMOOTHIES

Berry Yogurt Smoothie GF EF 18
Cool It Down Smoothie GF EF 20
PSL Redo GF EF 22
Cacao Coffee Boost GF EF 24
Pear Basil Cucumber Smoothie GF EF 26
Superfood Smoothie GF EF 28
Minty Cacao Green Smoothie GF EF 30
Peachy Keen Smoothie GF EF 32
Tropical Bliss Smoothie GF EF 34

*most smoothies can be made dairy free by substituting pea protein for whey protein powder

BREAKFASTS

Chard Gruyere Frittata GF KF 38
Migas with Spinach and Peppers GF 40
Broccoli Cheddar Frittata GF KF 42
Sweet potato Turkey Sausage Kale Breakfast Casserole GF 44
Green Eggs and Ham GF KF 46
Plantain Collagen Pancakes GF 48
Coco-NOatmeal GF KF 50
Overnight Oatmeal EF 52
Blueberry Flaxseed Overnight Oatmeal EF 54
Paleo Pumpkin Spice Muffins GF 56
Balanced Banana Walnut Muffins 58

SALADS

Minty Beet Almond Salad with Goat Cheese `GF` `EF` 62

Watermelon Feta Mint Salad `GF` `EF` 64

Fresh Herb Tahini Salad `GF` `EF` `KF` 66

Kale Cannellini Salad `GF` `EF` 68

Mediterranean Chickpea Salad `GF` `EF` `DF` 70

Kale Aphrodisiac Salad `GF` `EF` `DF` 72

Zesty Citrus Cabbage Slaw `GF` `EF` `DF` 74

Carrot Beet Salad `GF` `EF` `DF` 76

Avocado, Cucumber, Tomato Salad `GF` `EF` `DF` `KF` 78

Ginger Pear Salad with Maple Glazed Salmon `GF` `EF` `DF` 80

Blueberry Pistachio Chevre Salad `GF` `EF` 82

SOUPS

Black Bean Soup with Rotisserie Chicken `GF` `EF` `DF` 86

Turkey Wild Rice Soup `EF` `DF` 88

Curried Pumpkin Soup `GF` `EF` 90

Tex-Mex Chicken Soup `GF` `EF` 92

Avocado Cucumber Soup `GF` `EF` `DF` `KF` 94

Cauliflower Chowder `GF` `EF` `KF` 96

Tomato Basil Soup `GF` `EF` `DF` `KF` 98

SNACKS

Parm Crisps 3-ways `GF` `EF` `KF` 102

Wild Salmon Roll-ups `GF` `EF` `KF` 104

Greek Yogurt Dip with Raw Veggies `GF` `EF` `KF` 106

Beet Hummus `GF` `EF` `DF` 108

Simple Caprese Stack up `GF` `EF` `KF` 110

Simple Dressed Avocado `GF` `EF` `DF` `KF` 112

Kale Chips `GF` `EF` `DF` (ranch only) `KF` 114

Herb Roasted Nuts `GF` `EF` `DF` `KF` 116

Blueberry Pumpkin Seed Oat Bars 118

ENTREES

Seafood Entrees

Grilled Shrimp Skewers `GF` `EF` `DF` `KF` 122

Pesto Crusted Halibut `GF` `EF` `KF` 124

Asparagus and Prosciutto Saute with Seared Scallops `GF` `EF` `KF` 126

Maple Glazed Salmon `GF` `EF` `DF` 128

Miso-glazed Salmon with Gingery Vegetable Stir-fry `GF` `EF` `DF` 130

RED MEAT ENTREES

Colorful Soba Noodle Salad with Seared Buffalo EF DF 132
Seared Sirloin with Cherry Wine Reduction GF DF 134
Spaghetti Squash Casserole GF EF KF 138
Spicy Grass-fed Beef Stir-fry GF EF DF 140
Grass-fed Garlic and Kale Meatloaf DF 142
Slow Cooker Carnitas EF DF KF 144
Bourbon Peach Tenderloin GF EF 146

POULTRY ENTREES

Chicken Piccata GF KF 148
Pesto Turkey Meatballs and Roasted Vegetables GF KF 150
Tarragon Roasted Chicken and Vegetables GF EF DF KF 152
Mustard Chicken Thighs GF EF KF 154
Pan Seared Chicken with Tomato Jam GF EF KF 156
Curry Mango Chicken Salad GF EF 158
Broccoli Kale Chicken Dijon GF EF KF 160

VEGGIE SIDES

Buffalo Cauliflower GF EF KF 164
Braised Greens GF EF KF 166
Roasted Balsamic Vegetables GF EF DF KF 168
Rosemary Roasted Yukon Gold Potatoes GF EF 170
Caramelized Carrots with Basil and Honey GF EF DF 172
Chili Roasted Sweet Potatoes GF EF DF 174
Simple Roasted Asparagus GF EF KF 176
Sweet and Sour Vegetables GF EF DF KF 178

INDULGENCES

Cocoa Chia Bliss Bites GF EF DF 182
Cocoa Roasted Almonds GF DF 184
Gingered Apple Crumble EF 186
Mango Chia Coconut Pudding GF EF 188
Pumpkin Chia Seed Pudding GF EF DF 190
Raw Walnut Fudge GF EF DF 192
Coconut Poached Pears GF EF DF 194
Blueberry Spinach Cobbler EF 196
Greek Yogurt Cheesecake Bars EF 198
Goat Cheese Peach Tart GF 200
Black Bean Brownies with Walnuts and Chocolate Chunks GF EF DF 202
Banana Chocolate Ice Cream GF EF 204
Avocado Chocolate Mousse GF EF DF 206
Grain-Free Blueberry Pecan Cookies GF DF 208

THERAPEUTIC FOODS

Chicken Bone Broth GF EF KF 212

Grass-fed Beef Knuckle Broth GF EF DF KF 214

Bone Broth 3-ways GF EF KF 216

Coconut Ginger Mango Gelatin GF EF DF KF 218

Cranberry Gelatin GF EF DF KF 220

Ginger Zinger Matcha Whip GF EF KF 222

Water Infusions GF EF DF KF 224

DRESSINGS AND SAUCES:

Pumpkin Seed Pesto GF EF DF KF 228

Gingery Miso Sauce GF EF DF KF 230

Zingy Ginger Dressing GF EF DF KF 232

Rustic Balsamic Dressing GF EF DF KF 234

Simple Balsamic Vinaigrette GF EF DF KF 236

Blueberry Vinaigrette GF EF DF KF 238

Tahini-Lemon Dressing GF EF DF 240

Bright Minty Pepper Dressing & Marinade GF EF DF KF 242

Zesty Citrus Dressing GF EF DF 244

Week 1
1200 calories

	Day 1	Day 2	Day 3	Day 4	Day 5
Breakfast 7:00 am	Chard Gruyere Frittata 1 serving	Berry Yogurt Smoothie 1 serving	Chard Gruyere Frittata 1 serving	Berry Yogurt Smoothie 1 serving	Chard Gruyere Frittata 1 serving
Snack 10:00 am	Balanced Banana Walnut Muffin 1 muffin 1 tsp grass-fed butter	**Apple and Nut Butter** 1 medium apple 2 tsp fresh ground almond butter	Balanced Banana Walnut Muffin 1 muffin 1 tsp grass fed butter	**Apple and Nut Butter** 1 medium apple 2 tsp fresh ground almond butter	Balanced Banana Walnut Muffin 1 muffin 1 tsp grass fed butter
Lunch 12:30-1 pm	Black Bean Soup with Rotisserie Chicken and Simple Roasted Asparagus 1 serving each	Miso-glazed Salmon with Gingery Vegetable Stir-fry 1 serving	Grass-fed Garlic and Kale Meatloaf with Chili Roasted Sweet Potatoes 1 serving each	Black Bean Soup with Rotisserie Chicken and Simple Roasted Asparagus 1 serving each	Miso-glazed Salmon with Gingery Vegetable Stir-fry 1 serving
Snack 3:30 pm	Kale Chips 1 serving	**Raw Mixed Nuts** ¼ cup	Kale Chips 1 serving	**Raw Mixed Nuts** ¼ cup	Kale Chips 1 serving
Dinner 6:00-7 pm	Grass-fed Garlic and Kale Meatloaf with Chili Roasted Sweet Potatoes 1 serving each	Black Bean Soup with Rotisserie Chicken and Simple Roasted Asparagus 1 serving each	Miso-glazed Salmon with Gingery Vegetable Stir-fry 1 serving	Grass-fed Garlic and Kale Meatloaf with Chili Roasted Sweet Potatoes 1 serving each	Black Bean Soup with Rotisserie Chicken and Simple Roasted Asparagus 1 serving each

Week 1
1800 calories

	Day 1	Day 2	Day 3	Day 4	Day 5
Breakfast **7:00 am**	Chard Gruyere Frittata 1.5 servings	Berry Yogurt Smoothie 1 serving 1 egg	Chard Gruyere Frittata 1.5 servings	Berry Yogurt Smoothie 1 serving 1 egg	Chard Gruyere Frittata 1.5 servings
Snack **10:00 am**	Balanced Banana Nut Muffin 1 muffin 2 tsp grass fed butter	Apple and Nut Butter 1 medium apple 1 Tbsp fresh ground almond butter	Balanced Banana Nut Muffin 1 muffin 2 tsp grass fed butter	Apple and Nut Butter 1 medium apple 1 Tbsp fresh ground almond butter	Balanced Banana Nut Muffin 1 muffin 2 tsp grass fed butter
Lunch **12:30-1 pm**	Black Bean Soup with Rotisserie Chicken and Simple Roasted Asparagus 1.5 servings each	Miso-glazed Salmon with Gingery Vegetable Stir-fry 1.5 servings	Grass-fed Garlic and Kale Meatloaf with Chili Roasted Sweet Potatoes 1.5 servings each	Black Bean Soup with Rotisserie Chicken and Simple Roasted Asparagus 1.5 servings each	Miso-glazed Salmon with Gingery Vegetable Stir-fry 1.5 servings
Snack **3:30 pm**	Kale Chips 2 servings	Raw Mixed Nuts 1/3 cup	Kale Chips 2 servings	Raw Mixed Nuts 1/3 cup	Kale Chips 2 servings
Dinner **6:00-7 pm**	Grass-fed Garlic and Kale Meatloaf with Chili Roasted Sweet Potatoes 1.5 servings each	Black Bean Soup with Rotisserie Chicken and Simple Roasted Asparagus 1.5 servings each	Miso-glazed Salmon with Gingery Vegetable Stir-fry 1.5 servings	Grass-fed Garlic and Kale Meatloaf with Chili Roasted Sweet Potatoes 1.5 servings each	Black Bean Soup with Rotisserie Chicken and Simple Roasted Asparagus 1.5 servings each

Week 2
1200 calories

	Day 1	Day 2	Day 3	Day 4	Day 5
Breakfast 7:00 am	Migas with Spinach and Peppers 1 serving	Cacao Coffee Boost Smoothie 1 serving	Migas with Spinach and Peppers 1 serving	Cacao Coffee Boost Smoothie 1 serving	Migas with Spinach and Peppers 1 serving
Snack 10:00 am	Seeds and Fruit 1 Tbsp pumpkin seeds 1 medium pear	Celery and Nut butter 1 Cup Celery 2 tsp fresh ground almond butter	Seeds and Fruit 1 Tbsp pumpkin seeds 1 medium pear	Celery and Nut butter 1 Cup Celery 2 tsp fresh ground almond butter	Seeds and Fruit 1 Tbsp pumpkin seeds 1 medium pear
Lunch 12:30-1 pm	Avocado, Cucumber, Tomato Salad with Tuna 1 serving 4 Tbsp tuna	Spicy Grass-fed Beef Stir-fry 1 serving	Broccoli Kale Chicken Dijon 1 serving	Avocado, Cucumber, Tomato Salad with Tuna 1 serving 4 Tbsp tuna	Spicy Grass-fed Beef Stir-fry 1 serving
Snack 3:30 pm	Strawberries and Walnuts 6 walnuts ½ cup strawberries	Caramelized Carrots with Basil and Honey 1 serving 4 oz sliced turkey meat rolled up	Strawberries and Walnuts 6 walnuts ½ cup strawberries	Caramelized Carrots with Basil and Honey 1 serving 4 oz sliced turkey meat rolled up	Strawberries and Walnuts 6 walnuts ½ cup strawberries
Dinner 6:00-7 pm	Broccoli Kale Chicken Dijon 1 serving	Avocado, Cucumber, Tomato Salad with Tuna 1 serving 4 Tbsp tuna	Spicy Grass-fed Beef Stir-fry 1 serving	Broccoli Kale Chicken Dijon 1 serving	Avocado, Cucumber, Tomato Salad with Tuna 1 serving 4 Tbsp tuna

Week 2
1800 calories

	Day 1	Day 2	Day 3	Day 4	Day 5
Breakfast 7:00 am	Migas with Spinach and Peppers 1.5 servings	Cacao Coffee Boost Smoothie 1 serving	Migas with Spinach and Peppers 1.5 servings	Cacao Coffee Boost Smoothie 1 serving	Migas with Spinach and Peppers 1.5 servings
Snack 10:00 am	Seeds and Fruit 2 Tbsp pumpkin seeds 1 medium pear	Celery and Nut butter 2 cups celery 1-1.5 Tbsp fresh ground almond butter	Seeds and Fruit 2 Tbsp pumpkin seeds 1 medium pear	Celery and Nut butter 2 cups celery 1-1.5 Tbsp fresh ground almond butter	Seeds and Fruit 2 Tbsp pumpkin seeds 1 medium pear
Lunch 12:30-1 pm	Avocado, Cucumber, Tomato Salad with Tuna 1 serving 6 Tbsp tuna	Spicy Grass-fed Beef Stir-fry 1 serving	Broccoli Kale Chicken Dijon 1.5 servings	Avocado, Cucumber, Tomato Salad with Tuna 1 serving 6 Tbsp tuna	Spicy Grass-fed Beef Stir-fry 1 serving
Snack 3:30 pm	Strawberries and Walnuts 8 walnuts ¾ cup strawberries	Caramelized Carrots with Basil and Honey 1.5 servings 5 oz sliced turkey meat rolled up	Strawberries and Walnuts 8 walnuts ¾ cup strawberries	Caramelized Carrots with Basil and Honey 1 serving 4 oz sliced turkey meat rolled up	Strawberries and Walnuts 8 walnuts ¾ cup strawberries
Dinner 6:00-7 pm	Broccoli Kale Chicken Dijon 1.5 servings	Avocado, Cucumber, Tomato Salad with Tuna 1 serving 6 Tbsp tunc	Spicy Grass-fed Beef Stir-fry 1 serving	Broccoli Kale Chicken Dijon 1 serving	Avocado, Cucumber, Tomato Salad with Tuna 1 serving 6 Tbsp tuna

Week 3
1200 calories

	Day 1	Day 2	Day 3	Day 4	Day 5
Breakfast 7:00 am	Overnight Oats 1 serving	Tropical Bliss Smoothie 1 serving	Overnight Oats 1 serving	Tropical Bliss Smoothie 1 serving	Overnight Oats 1 serving
Snack 10:00 am	Avocado and Sea Salt ¼ avocado sprinkle sea salt	Hard Boiled Eggs and Apple 1 eggs 1 medium apple	Avocado and Sea Salt ¼ avocado sprinkle sea salt	Hard Boiled Eggs and Apple 1 eggs 1 medium apple	Avocado and Sea Salt ¼ avocado sprinkle sea salt
Lunch 12:30-1 pm	Carrot Beet Salad 1 serving 4 oz canned tuna (or lean protein of choice)	Curry Mango Chicken Salad 1 serving	Ginger Pear Salad with Maple Glazed Salmon 1 serving	Carrot Beet Salad 1 serving 4 oz canned tuna (or lean protein of choice)	Curry Mango Chicken Salad 1 serving
Snack 3:30 pm	Banana Chocolate Ice Cream 1 serving	Yogurt and Chia Seeds 8 oz yogurt (ie Nancy's Organic) 1 Tbsp chia seeds	Banana Chocolate Ice Cream 1 serving	Yogurt and Chia Seeds 8 oz yogurt (ie Nancy's Organic) 1 Tbsp chia seeds	Banana Chocolate Ice Cream 1 serving
Dinner 6:00-7 pm	Ginger Pear Salad with Maple Glazed Salmon 1 serving	Carrot Beet Salad 1 serving 4 oz canned tuna (or lean protein of choice)	Curry Mango Chicken Salad 1 serving	Ginger Pear Salad with Maple Glazed Salmon 1 serving	Carrot Beet Salad (⅓ of recipe) 6 oz canned tuna (or lean protein of choice)

Week 3
1800 calories

	Day 1	Day 2	Day 3	Day 4	Day 5
Breakfast **7:00 am**	Overnight Oats 1 serving 1 egg over easy	Tropical Bliss Smoothie 1 serving	Overnight Oats 1 serving 1 egg over easy	Tropical Bliss Smoothie 1 serving	Overnight Oats 1 serving 1 egg over easy
Snack **10:00 am**	Avocado and Sea Salt ½ avocado sprinkle sea salt	Hard Boiled Eggs and Apple 2 eggs 1 medium apple	Avocado and Sea Salt ½ avocado sprinkle sea salt	Hard Boiled Eggs and Apple 2 eggs 1 medium apple	Avocado and Sea Salt ½ avocado sprinkle sea salt
Lunch **12:30-1 pm**	Carrot Beet Salad 1.5 servings 6 oz canned tuna (or lean protein of choice)	Curry Mango Chicken Salad 1.5 servings	Maple Glazed Salmon Salad with Zing Ginger Dressing 1.5 servings	Carrot Beet Salad 1.5 servings 6 oz canned tuna (or lean protein of choice)	Curry Mango Chicken Salad 1.5 servings
Snack **3:30 pm**	Banana Chocolate Ice Cream 1 serving	Yogurt and Chia Seeds 8 oz yogurt (ie Nancy's Organic) 1 Tbsp chia seeds	Banana Chocolate Ice Cream 1 serving	Yogurt and Chia Seeds 8 oz yogurt (ie Nancy's Organic) 1 Tbsp chia seeds	Banana Chocolate Ice Cream 1 serving
Dinner **6:00-7 pm**	Maple Glazed Salmon Salad with Zing Ginger Dressing 1.5 servings	Carrot Beet Salad 1.5 servings 6 oz canned tuna (or lean protein of choice)	Curry Mango Chicken Salad 1.5 servings	Maple Glazed Salmon Salad with Zing Ginger Dressing 1.5 servings	Carrot Beet Salad 1.5 servings 6 oz canned tuna (or lean protein of choice)

Week 4
1200 calories

	Day 1	Day 2	Day 3	Day 4	Day 5
Breakfast 7:00 am	**Paleo Pumpkin Spice Muffin** 1 serving 1 tsp grass-fed butter 6 oz Greek yogurt on the side	**Blueberry Pumpkin Seed Oat Bar** 1 bar	**Paleo Pumpkin Spice Muffin** 1 serving 1 tsp grass-fed butter 6 oz Greek yogurt on the side	**Blueberry Pumpkin Seed Oat Bar** 1 bar	**Paleo Pumpkin Spice Muffin** 1 serving 1 tsp grass-fed butter 6 oz Greek yogurt on the side
Snack 10:00 am	**Blackberries and Nuts** ½ cup blackberries 5 macadamia nuts	**Brown Rice Cake and Peanut Butter** 1 brown rice cake 1 Tbsp peanut butter	**Blackberries and Nuts** ½ cup blackberries 5 macadamia nuts	**Brown Rice Cake and Peanut Butter** 1 brown rice cake 1 Tbsp peanut butter	**Blackberries and Nuts** ½ cup blackberries 5 macadamia nuts
Lunch 12:30-1 pm	**Turkey Wild Rice Soup** 1 serving	**Bourbon Peach Tenderloin** 1 serving 2 cups mixed greens	**Zesty Citrus Cabbage Slaw** 1 serving 4 oz chicken	**Turkey Wild Rice Soup** 1 serving	**Bourbon Peach Tenderloin** 1 serving 2 cups mixed greens
Snack 3:30 pm	**Grapes and Cheese** 15 grapes 1 oz raw aged cheese	**Orange and Cashews** 1 medium orange 8-10 cashews	**Grapes and Cheese** 15 grapes 1 oz raw aged cheese	**Orange and Cashews** 1 medium orange 8-10 cashews	**Grapes and Cheese** 15 grapes 1 oz raw aged cheese
Dinner 6:00-7 pm	**Zesty Citrus Cabbage Slaw** 1 serving 4 oz chicken	**Turkey Wild Rice Soup** 1 serving	**Bourbon Peach Tenderloin** 1 serving 2 cups mixed greens	**Zesty Citrus Cabbage Slaw** 1 serving 4 oz chicken	**Turkey Wild Rice Soup** 1 serving

Week 4
1800 calories

	Day 1	Day 2	Day 3	Day 4	Day 5
Breakfast 7:00 am	Paleo Pumpkin Spice Muffin 1 serving 2 tsp grass-fed butter 8 oz Greek yogurt on the side	Blueberry Pumpkin Seed Oat Bar 1.5 bars	Paleo Pumpkin Spice Muffin 1 serving 2 tsp grass-fed butter 8 oz Greek yogurt on the side	Blueberry Pumpkin Seed Oat Bar 1.5 bars	Paleo Pumpkin Spice Muffin 1 serving 2 tsp grass-fed butter 8 oz Greek yogurt on the side
Snack 10:00 am	Blackberries and Nuts ¾ cup blackberries 8 macadamia nuts	Brown Rice Cake and Peanut Butter 1 brown rice cake 2 Tbsp peanut butter	Blackberries and Nuts ¾ cup blackberries 8 macadamia nuts	Brown Rice Cake and Peanut Butter 1 brown rice cake 2 Tbsp peanut butter	Blackberries and Nuts ¾ cup blackberries 8 macadamia nuts
Lunch 12:30-1 pm	Turkey Wild Rice Soup 2 servings	Bourbon Peach Tenderloin 1 serving 3 cups mixed greens	Zesty Citrus Cabbage Slaw 2 servings 6 oz chicken	Turkey Wild Rice Soup 2 servings	Bourbon Peach Tenderloin 1 serving 3 cups mixed greens
Snack 3:30 pm	Grapes and Cheese 30 grapes 2 oz raw aged cheese	Orange and Cashews 1 medium orange 12-14 cashews	Grapes and Cheese 30 grapes 2 oz raw aged cheese	Orange and Cashews 1 medium orange 12-14 cashews	Grapes and Cheese 30 grapes 2 oz raw aged cheese
Dinner 6:00-7 pm	Zesty Citrus Cabbage Slaw 2 servings 6 oz chicken	Turkey Wild Rice Soup 2 servings	Bourbon Peach Tenderloin 1 serving 3 cups mixed greens	Zesty Citrus Cabbage Slaw 2 servings 6 oz chicken	Turkey Wild Rice Soup 2 servings

Week 5
1200 calories

	Day 1	Day 2	Day 3	Day 4	Day 5
Breakfast 7:00 am	Broccoli Cheddar Frittata 1 serving	Cottage Cheese and Peach ½ cup cottage cheese (ie Organic Valley) 1 peach	Broccoli Cheddar Frittata 1 serving	Cottage Cheese and Peach ½ cup cottage cheese (ie Organic Valley) 1 peach	Broccoli Cheddar Frittata 1 serving
Snack 10:00 am	Fruit and Nuts 1 medium orange ⅛ cup pistachios	Melon and Prosciutto 1 cup melon 1 oz prosciutto	Fruit and Nuts 1 medium orange ⅛ cup pistachios	Melon and Prosciutto 1 cup melon 1 oz prosciutto	Fruit and Nuts 1 medium orange ⅛ cup pistachios
Lunch 12:30-1 pm	Kale Aphrodisiac Salad 1 serving 3 oz chicken or protein of choice	Mustard Chicken Things with Buffalo Cauliflower 1 serving each	Spaghetti Squash Casserole 1 serving	Kale Aphrodisiac Salad 1 serving 3 oz chicken or protein of choice	Mustard Chicken Things with Buffalo Cauliflower 1 serving each
Snack 3:30 pm	Parmesan Crisps 1 serving	Black Bean Brownies with Walnuts and Chocolate Chunks 1 brownie	Parmesan Crisps 1 serving	Black Bean Brownies with Walnuts and Chocolate Chunks 1 brownie	Parmesan Crisps 1 serving
Dinner 6:00-7 pm	Spaghetti Squash Casserole 1 serving	Kale Aphrodisiac Salad 1 serving 3 oz chicken or protein of choice	Mustard Chicken Things with Buffalo Cauliflower 1 serving each	Spaghetti Squash Casserole 1 serving	Kale Aphrodisiac Salad 1 serving 3 oz chicken or protein of choice

Week 5
1800 calories

	Day 1	Day 2	Day 3	Day 4	Day 5
Breakfast 7:00 am	**Broccoli Cheddar Frittata** 1 serving 1 cup berries	**Cottage Cheese and Peach** ¾ cup cottage cheese (ie Organic Valley) 1 peach	Broccoli Cheddar Frittata 1 serving 1 cup berries	**Cottage Cheese and Peach** ¾ cup cottage cheese (ie Organic Valley) 1 peach	Broccoli Cheddar Frittata 1 serving 1 cup berries
Snack 10:00 am	**Fruit and Nuts** 1 medium orange ¼ cup pistachios	**Melon and Prosciutto** 1 cup melon 2 oz prosciutto	**Fruit and Nuts** 1 medium orange ¼ cup pistachios	**Melon and Prosciutto** 1 cup melon 2 oz prosciutto	**Fruit and Nuts** 1 medium orange ¼ cup pistachios
Lunch 12:30-1 pm	Kale Aphrodisiac Salad 1.5 servings 5 oz chicken or protein of choice	Mustard Chicken Things with Buffalo Cauliflower 1.5 servings each	Spaghetti Squash Casserole 1.5 servings	Kale Aphrodisiac Salad 1.5 servings 5 oz chicken or protein of choice	Mustard Chicken Things with Buffalo Cauliflower 1.5 servings each
Snack 3:30 pm	Parmesan Crisps 2 servings	Black Bean Brownies with Walnuts 1 brownie	Parmesan Crisps 2 servings	Black Bean Brownies with Walnuts 1 brownie	Parmesan Crisps 2 servings
Dinner 6:00-7 pm	Spaghetti Squash Casserole 1.5 servings	Kale Aphrodisiac Salad 1.5 servings 5 oz chicken or protein of choice	Mustard Chicken Things with Buffalo Cauliflower 1.5 servings each	Spaghetti Squash Casserole 1.5 servings	Kale Aphrodisiac Salad 5 oz chicken or protein of choice 2 cups Kale Salad

Week 6
1200 calories

	Day 1	Day 2	Day 3	Day 4	Day 5
Breakfast 7:00 am	Plantain Collagen Pancakes 1 serving 1 Tbsp grade b maple syrup	Pear Basil Cucumber Smoothie 1 serving	Plantain Collagen Pancakes 1 serving 1 Tbsp grade b maple syrup	Pear Basil Cucumber Smoothie 1 serving	Plantain Collagen Pancakes 1 serving 1 Tbsp grade b maple syrup
Snack 10:00 am	Cheese and Fruit 1 pear 1 oz goat cheese	Eggs and Fruit 1 hardboiled egg ½ cup berries	Cheese and Fruit 1 pear 1 oz goat cheese	Eggs and Fruit 1 hardboiled egg ½ cup berries	Cheese and Fruit 1 pear 1 oz goat cheese
Lunch 12:30-1 pm	Mediterranean Chickpea Salad with spinach and Rotisserie Chicken 1 serving 3 oz chicken	Tarragon Roasted Chicken and Vegetables 1 serving	Curried Pumpkin Soup 1 serving 2 oz roasted turkey	Mediterranean Chickpea Salad with spinach and Rotisserie Chicken 1 serving 3 oz chicken	Tarragon Roasted Chicken and Vegetables 1 serving
Snack 3:30 pm	Herb Roasted Nuts 1 serving	Simple Dressed Avocado 1 serving	Herb Roasted Nuts 1 serving	Simple Dressed Avocado 1 serving	Herb Roasted Nuts 1 serving
Dinner 6:00-7 pm	Curried Pumpkin Soup 1 serving 2 oz roasted turkey	Mediterranean Chickpea Salad with spinach and Rotisserie Chicken 1 serving 3 oz chicken	Tarragon Roasted Chicken and Vegetables 1 serving	Curried Pumpkin Soup 1 serving 2 oz roasted turkey	Mediterranean Chickpea Salad with spinach and Rotisserie Chicken 1 serving 3 oz chicken

Week 6
1800 calories

	Day 1	Day 2	Day 3	Day 4	Day 5
Breakfast 7:00 am	Plantain Collagen Pancakes 1.5 servings 1.5 Tbsp grade b maple syrup	Pear Basil Cucumber Smoothie 1.5 servings	Plantain Collagen Pancakes 1.5 servings 1.5 Tbsp grade b maple syrup	Pear Basil Cucumber Smoothie 1.5 servings	Plantain Collagen Pancakes 1.5 servings 1.5 Tbsp grade b maple syrup
Snack 10:00 am	Cheese and Fruit 1 pear 2 oz goat cheese	Eggs and Fruit 2 hardboiled eggs 1 cup berries	Cheese and Fruit 1 pear 2 oz goat cheese	Eggs and Fruit 2 hardboiled eggs 1 cup berries	Cheese and Fruit 1 pear 2 oz goat cheese
Lunch 12:30-1 pm	Mediterranean Chickpea Salad with spinach and Rotisserie Chicken 1 serving 5 oz chicken	Tarragon Roasted Chicken and Vegetables 1.5 servings	Curried Pumpkin Soup 1.5 servings 3 oz roasted turkey	Mediterranean Chickpea Salad with spinach and Rotisserie Chicken 1 serving 5 oz chicken	Tarragon Roasted Chicken and Vegetables 1.5 servings
Snack 3:30 pm	Herb Roasted Nuts 1.5 servings	Simple Dressed Avocado 2 servings	Herb Roasted Nuts 1.5 servings	Simple Dressed Avocado 2 servings	Herb Roasted Nuts 1.5 servings
Dinner 6:00-7 pm	Curried Pumpkin Soup 1.5 servings 3 oz roasted turkey	Mediterranean Chickpea Salad with spinach and Rotisserie Chicken 1 serving 5 oz chicken	Tarragon Roasted Chicken and Vegetables 1.5 servings	Curried Pumpkin Soup 1.5 servings 3 oz roasted turkey	Mediterranean Chickpea Salad with spinach and Rotisserie Chicken 1 serving 5 oz chicken

Week 7
1200 calories

	Day 1	Day 2	Day 3	Day 4	Day 5
Breakfast 7:00 am	Sweet potato Turkey Sausage Kale Breakfast Casserole 1 serving	Cool it Down Smoothie 1 serving	Sweet potato Turkey Sausage Kale Breakfast Casserole	Cool it Down Smoothie 1 serving	Sweet potato Turkey Sausage Kale Breakfast Casserole 1 serving
Snack 10:00 am	Chili Powder Pumpkin Seeds 2 Tbsp serving 1 cup pumpkin seeds 2 teaspoons olive oil 1 tablespoon chili powder 1 teaspoon celtic sea salt (adjust to your taste, I like things salty) Cook over medium heat for 3-5 mins	Goat Cheese Peach Tart 1 serving	Chili Powder Pumpkin Seeds 2 Tbsp serving 1 cup pumpkin seeds 2 teaspoons olive oil 1 tablespoon chili powder 1 teaspoon celtic sea salt (adjust to your taste, I like things salty) Cook over medium heat for 3-5 mins	Goat Cheese Peach Tart 1 serving	Chili Powder Pumpkin Seeds 2 Tbsp serving 1 cup pumpkin seeds 2 teaspoons olive oil 1 tablespoon chili powder 1 teaspoon celtic sea salt (adjust to your taste, I like things salty) Cook over medium heat for 3-5 mins
Lunch 12:30-1 pm	Tex-Mex Chicken Soup 1 serving sprinkle cheese (1 Tbsp)	Miso Glazed Salmon with Gingery Vegetable Stir Fry 1 serving	Wild Salmon Roll Ups with side salad 2 servings roll ups	Tex-Mex Chicken Soup 1 serving sprinkle cheese (1 Tbsp)	Miso Glazed Salmon with Gingery Vegetable Stir Fry 1 serving
Snack 3:30 pm	Chai Kefir 6 oz cup plan kefir ½ tsp cinnamon ½ tsp honey	Greek Yogurt Dip with Raw Veggies 1 cup veggies 1 serving dip	Chai Kefir 6 oz cup plan kefir ½ tsp cinnamon ½ tsp honey	Greek Yogurt Dip with Raw Veggies 1 cup veggies 1 serving dip	Chai Kefir 6 oz cup plan kefir ½ tsp cinnamon ½ tsp honey
Dinner 6:00-7 pm	Wild Salmon Roll Ups with side salad 2 servings roll ups	Tex-Mex Chicken Soup 1 serving sprinkle cheese (1 Tbsp)	Miso Glazed Salmon with Gingery Vegetable Stir Fry 1 serving	Wild Salmon Roll Ups with side salad 2 servings roll ups	Tex-Mex Chicken Soup 1 serving sprinkle cheese (1 Tbsp)

Week 7

1800 calories

	Day 1	Day 2	Day 3	Day 4	Day 5
Breakfast 7:00 am	Sweet potato Turkey Sausage Kale Breakfast Casserole 1.5 servings	Cool it Down Smoothie 1.5 servings	Sweet potato Turkey Sausage Kale Breakfast Casserole 1.5 servings	Cool it Down Smoothie 1.5 servings	Sweet potato Turkey Sausage Kale Breakfast Casserole 1.5 servings
Snack 10:00 am	**Chili Powder Pumpkin Seeds** 3 Tbsp serving 1 cup pumpkin seeds 2 teaspoons olive oil 1 tablespoon chili powder 1 teaspoon celtic sea salt (adjust to your taste, I like things salty) Cook over medium heat for 3-5 mins	Goat Cheese Peach Tart 1 serving	**Chili Powder Pumpkin Seeds** 3 Tbsp serving 1 cup pumpkin seeds 2 teaspoons olive oil 1 tablespoon chili powder 1 teaspoon celtic sea salt (adjust to your taste, I like things salty) Cook over medium heat for 3-5 mins	Goat Cheese Peach Tart 1 serving	**Chili Powder Pumpkin Seeds** 3 Tbsp serving 1 cup pumpkin seeds 2 teaspoons olive oil 1 tablespoon chili powder 1 teaspoon celtic sea salt (adjust to your taste, I like things salty) Cook over medium heat for 3-5 mins
Lunch 12:30-1 pm	Tex-Mex Chicken Soup 1.5 servings sprinkle cheese (1.5 Tbsp)	Miso Glazed Salmon with Gingery Vegetable Stir Fry 1.5 servings	Wild Salmon Roll Ups with side salad 3 servings roll ups	Tex-Mex Chicken Soup 1.5 servings sprinkle cheese (1.5 Tbsp.)	Miso Glazed Salmon with Gingery Vegetable Stir Fry 1.5 servings
Snack 3:30 pm	**Chai Kefir** 8 oz plan kefir ½ tsp cinnamon ½ tsp honey	Greek Yogurt Dip with Raw Veggies 1 cup veggies 1.5 servings dip	**Chai Kefir** 8 oz plan kefir ½ tsp cinnamon ½ tsp honey	Greek Yogurt Dip with Raw Veggies 1 cup veggies 1.5 servings dip	**Chai Kefir** 8 oz plan kefir ½ tsp cinnamon ½ tsp honey
Dinner 6:00-7 pm	Wild Salmon Roll Ups with side salad 3 servings roll ups	Tex-Mex Chicken Soup 1/5 of recipe sprinkle cheese (1.5 Tbsp)	Miso Glazed Salmon with Gingery Vegetable Stir Fry 1.5 servings	Wild Salmon Roll Ups with side salad 3 servings roll ups	Tex-Mex Chicken Soup 1/5 of recipe sprinkle cheese (1.5 Tbsp)

Week 8
1200 calories

	Day 1	Day 2	Day 3	Day 4	Day 5
Breakfast 7:00 am	Peachy Keen Smoothie 1 serving	Eggs and Bacon 2 eggs 1 slice bacon ½ cup sauteed Kale	Peachy Keen Smoothie 1 serving	Eggs and Bacon 2 eggs 1 slice bacon ½ cup sauteed Kale	Peachy Keen Smoothie 1 serving
Snack 10:00 am	Banana and Almond Butter ½ banana 1 Tbsp almond butter	Raspberries and Cream ½ cup raspberries 2 Tbsp Greek yogurt ½ tsp raw unfiltered honey (optional)	Banana and Almond Butter ½ banana 1 Tbsp almond butter	Raspberries and Cream ½ cup raspberries 2 Tbsp Greek yogurt ½ tsp raw unfiltered honey (optional)	Banana and Almond Butter ½ banana 1 Tbsp almond butter
Lunch 12:30-1 pm	Chicken Piccata 1 serving 1 cup green beans, blanched	Asparagus and Prosciutto Salad with Seared Scallops 1 serving	Pesto Turkey Meatballs w/ Roasted Balsamic Vegetables 1 serving each	Chicken Piccata with blanched Green Beans 1 serving 1 cup green beans	Asparagus and Prosciutto Salad with Seared Scallops 1 serving
Snack 3:30 pm	Greek Yogurt Cheesecake Bar 1 serving	Simple Caprese Stack Up 1 serving	Greek Yogurt Cheesecake Bar 1 serving	Simple Caprese Stack Up 1 serving	Greek Yogurt Cheesecake Bar 1 serving
Dinner 6:00-7 pm	Pesto Turkey Meatballs w/ Roasted Balsamic Vegetables 1 serving each	Chicken Piccata 1 serving 1 cup green beans, blanched	Asparagus and Prosciutto Salad with Seared Scallops 1 serving	Pesto Turkey Meatballs w/ Roasted Balsamic Vegetables 1 serving each	Chicken Piccata 1 serving 1 cup green beans, blanched

Week 8
1800 calories

	Day 1	Day 2	Day 3	Day 4	Day 5
Breakfast 7:00 am	Peachy Keen Smoothie 1 serving 1 hard boiled egg	Eggs and Bacon 3 eggs 1 slice bacon ¾ cup sauteed Kale	Peachy Keen Smoothie 1 serving 1 hard boiled egg	Eggs and Bacon 3 eggs 1 slice bacon ¾ cup sauteed Kale	Peachy Keen Smoothie 1 serving 1 hard boiled egg
Snack 10:00 am	Banana and Almond Butter 1 banana 1.5 Tbsp almond butter	Raspberries and Cream ¾ cup raspberries ¼ cup Greek yogurt ½ tsp raw unfiltered honey (optional)	Banana and Almond Butter 1 banana 1.5 Tbsp almond butter	Raspberries and Cream ¾ cup raspberries ¼ cup Greek yogurt ½ tsp raw unfiltered honey (optional)	Banana and Almond Butter 1 banana 1.5 Tbsp almond butter
Lunch 12:30-1 pm	Chicken Piccata 1.5 servings 1.5 cup green beans, blanched	Asparagus and Prosciutto Salad with Seared Scallops 1.5 servings	Pesto Turkey Meatballs w/ Roasted Vegetables 1.5 servings each	Chicken Piccata 1.5 servings 1.5 cup green beans, blanched	Asparagus and Prosciutto Salad with Seared Scallops 1.5 servings
Snack 3:30 pm	Greek Yogurt Cheesecake Bar 1.5 servings	Simple Caprese Stack Up 2 servings	Greek Yogurt Cheesecake Bar 1.5 servings	Simple Caprese Stack Up 2 servings	Greek Yogurt Cheesecake Bar 1.5 servings
Dinner 6:00-7 pm	Pesto Turkey Meatballs w/ Roasted Vegetables 1.5 servings each	Chicken Piccata 1.5 servings 1.5 cup green beans, blanched	Asparagus and Prosciutto Salad with Seared Scallops 1.5 servings	Pesto Turkey Meatballs w/ Roasted Vegetables 1.5 servings each	Chicken Piccata 1.5 servings 1.5 cup green beans, blanched

Week 9
1200 calories

	Day 1	Day 2	Day 3	Day 4	Day 5
Breakfast 7:00 am	Coco-NOatmeal 1 serving	**Southwestern Omelet** 2 eggs ¼ cup salsa 1 oz shredded cheese 1-2 Tbsp sautéed onion	Coco-NOatmeal 1 serving	**Southwestern Omelet** 2 eggs ¼ cup salsa 1 oz shredded cheese 1-2 Tbsp sautéed onion	Coco-NOatmeal 1 serving
Snack 10:00 am	Blueberry Spinach Cobbler 1 serving	**Cherries and Cream** ½ cup cherries ½ cup Greek yogurt	**Cottage Cheese and Pineapple** 6 oz cottage cheese ½ cup pineapple	**Cherries and Cream** ½ cup cherries ½ cup Greek yogurt	Blueberry Spinach Cobbler 1 serving
Lunch 12:30-1 pm	Avocado Cucumber Soup 1 serving 2 oz chicken	Pesto Crusted Halibut with Sweet and Sour sautéed vegetables 1 serving of each	**Seared Sirloin with Cherry Wine Reduction** 1 serving 2 cups sautéed spinach in 2 tsp butter	Avocado Cucumber Soup 1 serving 2 oz chicken	Pesto Crusted Halibut with Sweet and Sour sautéed vegetables 1 serving of each
Snack 3:30 pm	Roasted Beet Hummus with Vegetable Spears 1 serving	**Grilled Peaches** 1 peach halved coat with 1-2 tsp coconut oil grill on med-high heat for 4 min per side	Blueberry Spinach Cobbler 1 serving	**Grilled Peaches** 1 peach halved coat with 1-2 tsp coconut oil grill on med-high heat for 4 min per side	Roasted Beet Hummus with Vegetable Spears 1 serving
Dinner 6:00-7 pm	**Seared Sirloin with Cherry Wine Reduction** 1 serving 2 cups sautéed spinach in 2 tsp butter	**Seared Sirloin with Cherry Wine Reduction** 1 serving 2 cups sautéed spinach in 2 tsp butter	**Seared Sirloin with Cherry Wine Reduction** 1 serving 2 cups sautéed spinach in 2 tsp butter	Avocado Cucumber Soup 1 serving 2 oz chicken	Avocado Cucumber Soup 1 serving 2 oz chicken

Week 9
1800 calories

	Day 1	Day 2	Day 3	Day 4	Day 5
Breakfast 7:00 am	Coco-NOatmeal 1.5 servings	**Southwestern Omelet** 3 eggs ⅓ cup salsa 1-2 oz shredded cheese 1-2 Tbsp sautéed onion	Coco-NOatmeal 1.5 servings	**Southwestern Omelet** 3 eggs ⅓ cup salsa 1-2 oz shredded cheese 1-2 Tbsp sautéed onion	Coco-NOatmeal 1.5 servings
Snack 10:00 am	Blueberry Spinach Cobbler 1 serving	**Cherries and Cream** ½ cup cherries ¾ cup Greek yogurt	**Cottage Cheese and Pineapple** 8 oz cottage cheese ¾ cup pineapple	**Cherries and Cream** ½ cup cherries ¾ cup Greek yogurt	Blueberry Spinach Cobbler 1 serving
Lunch 12:30-1 pm	Avocado Cucumber Soup 1 serving 4 oz chicken	Pesto Crusted Halibut with Sweet and Sour sautéed vegetables 1.5 servings of each	Seared Sirloin with Cherry Wine Reduction 1 serving 2 cups spinach sautéed in 1 Tbsp butter	Avocado Cucumber Soup 1 serving 4 oz chicken	Pesto Crusted Halibut with Sweet and Sour sautéed vegetables 1.5 servings of each
Snack 3:30 pm	Roasted Beet Hummus with Vegetable Spears 2 servings	**Grilled Peaches** 1 peach halved coat with 2-3 tsp coconut oil grill on med-high heat for 4 min per side	Blueberry Spinach Cobbler 1 serving	**Grilled Peaches** 1 peach halved coat with 2-3 tsp coconut oil grill on med-high heat for 4 min per side	Roasted Beet Hummus with Vegetable Spears 2 servings
Dinner 6:00-7 pm	Seared Sirloin with Cherry Wine Reduction 1 serving 2 cups spinach sautéed in 1 Tbsp butter	Avocado Cucumber Soup 1 serving 4 oz chicken	Pesto Crusted Halibut with Sweet and Sour sautéed vegetables 1.5 servings of each	Seared Sirloin with Cherry Wine Reduction 1 serving 2 cups spinach sautéed in 1 Tbsp butter	Avocado Cucumber Soup 1 serving 4 oz chicken

Week 10
1200 calories

	Day 1	Day 2	Day 3	Day 4	Day 5
Breakfast 7:00 am	**Minty Cacao Green Smoothie** 1 serving	**Eggs and Spinach** 2 eggs over easy 1 tsp butter 1 cup sautéed spinach in 2 tsp butter	**Minty Cacao Green Smoothie** 1 serving	**Eggs and Spinach** 2 eggs over easy 1 tsp butter 1 cup sautéed spinach in 2 tsp butter	**Minty Cacao Green Smoothie** 1 serving
Snack 10:00 am	**Grapes and Cheese** 15 grapes 1 oz cheese	**Grapefruit and Yogurt** 1 grapefruit ½ cup Greek yogurt	Coconut Poached Pears 1 serving	**Grapefruit and Yogurt** 1 grapefruit ½ cup Greek yogurt	**Grapes and Cheese** 15 grapes 1 oz cheese
Lunch 12:30-1 pm	Blueberry Pistachio Chèvre Salad 1 serving	Kale Cannellini Salad 1 serving	Slow Cooker Carnitas 1 serving	Blueberry Pistachio Chèvre Salad 1 serving	Kale Cannellini Salad 1 serving
Snack 3:30 pm	**Turkey and an Apple** 1 apple 2 oz turkey	Coconut Poached Pears 1 serving	**Turkey and an Apple** 1 apple 2 oz turkey	Coconut Poached Pears 1 serving	**Turkey and an Apple** 1 apple 2 oz turkey
Dinner 6:00-7 pm	Slow Cooker Carnitas 1 serving	Blueberry Pistachio Chèvre Salad 1 serving	Kale Cannellini Salad 1 serving	Slow Cooker Carnitas 1 serving	Blueberry Pistachio Chèvre Salad 1 serving

Week 10
1800 calories

	Day 1	Day 2	Day 3	Day 4	Day 5
Breakfast 7:00 am	Minty Cacao Green Smoothie 2 servings	Eggs and Spinach 3 eggs over easy 2 tsp butter 1.5 cups sautéed spinach in 2 tsp butter	Minty Cacao Green Smoothie 2 servings	Eggs and Spinach 3 eggs over easy 2 tsp butter 1.5 cups sautéed spinach in 2 tsp butter	Minty Cacao Green Smoothie 2 servings
Snack 10:00 am	Grapes and Cheese 30 grapes 2 oz cheese	Grapefruit and Yogurt 1 grapefruit 1 cup Greek yogurt	Coconut Poached Pears 1.5 servings	Grapefruit and Yogurt 1 grapefruit 1 cup Greek yogurt	Grapes and Cheese 30 grapes 2 oz cheese
Lunch 12:30-1 pm	Blueberry Pistachio Chèvre Salad 1 serving	Kale Cannellini Salad 1.5 servings	Slow Cooker Carnitas 1.5 servings	Blueberry Pistachio Chèvre Salad 1 serving	Kale Cannellini Salad 1.5 servings
Snack 3:30 pm	Turkey and an Apple 1 apple 3 oz turkey	Coconut Poached Pears 1.5 servings	Turkey and an Apple 1 apple 3 oz turkey	Coconut Poached Pears 1.5 servings	Turkey and an Apple 1 apple 3 oz turkey
Dinner 6:00-7 pm	Slow Cooker Carnitas 1.5 servings	Blueberry Pistachio Chèvre Salad 1 serving	Kale Cannellini Salad 1.5 servings	Slow Cooker Carnitas 1.5 servings	Blueberry Pistachio Chèvre Salad 1 serving

Week 11
1200 calories

	Day 1	Day 2	Day 3	Day 4	Day 5
Breakfast 7:00 am	Green Eggs and Ham or Turkey 1 serving	PSL Redo 1 serving	Green Eggs and Ham or Turkey 1 serving	PSL Redo 1 serving	Green Eggs and Ham or Turkey 1 serving
Snack 10:00 am	Raw Walnut Fudge 1 serving	**Trail Mix** 8-10 nuts 1 Tbsp dried fruit mix (apricots, raisins etc) 1 piece 70% dark chocolate	Raw Walnut Fudge 1 serving	**Trail Mix** 8-10 nuts 1 Tbsp dried fruit mix (apricots, raisins etc) 1 piece 70% dark chocolate	Raw Walnut Fudge 1 serving
Lunch 12:30-1 pm	Tomato Basil Soup 1 serving ¼ avocado cubes on top	Watermelon Feta Mint Salad 1 serving 4 oz chicken	Tomato Basil Soup 1 serving ¼ avocado cubes on top	Watermelon Feta Mint Salad 1 serving 4 oz chicken	Tomato Basil Soup 1 serving ¼ avocado cubes on top
Snack 3:30 pm	Nut Butter and Brown Rice Cake 1 Tbsp Nut butter (almond, sunflower, etc) 1 Brown Rice Cake	Raw Walnut Fudge 1 serving	Nut Butter and Brown Rice Cake 1 Tbsp Nut butter (almond, sunflower, etc) 1 Brown Rice Cake	Raw Walnut Fudge 1 serving	Nut Butter and Brown Rice Cake 1 Tbsp Nut butter (almond, sunflower, etc)
Dinner 6:00-7 pm	Herby Tahini Salad with Grilled Shrimp Skewers 1 serving each	Cauliflower Chowder 1 cup soup	Herby Tahini Salad with Grilled Shrimp Skewers 1 serving each	Cauliflower Chowder 1 cup soup	Herby Tahini Salad with Grilled Shrimp Skewers 1 serving each

Week 11
1800 calories

	Day 1	Day 2	Day 3	Day 4	Day 5
Breakfast 7:00 am	Green Eggs and Ham or Turkey 1.5 servings	PSL Redo 1.5 servings	Green Eggs and Ham or Turkey 1.5 servings	PSL Redo 1.5 servings	Green Eggs and Ham or Turkey 1.5 servings
Snack 10:00 am	Raw Walnut Fudge 2 servings	**Trail Mix** 10-12 nuts 1.5 Tbsp dried fruit mix (apricots, raisins etc) 2 piece 70% dark chocolate	Raw Walnut Fudge 2 servings	**Trail Mix** 10-12 nuts 1.5 Tbsp dried fruit mix (apricots, raisins etc) 2 piece 70% dark chocolate	Raw Walnut Fudge 2 servings
Lunch 12:30-1 pm	Tomato Basil Soup 2 servings ½ avocado cubes on top	Watermelon Feta Mint Salad 1.5 servings 5 oz chicken	Tomato Basil Soup 2 servings ½ avocado cubes on top	Watermelon Feta Mint Salad 1.5 servings 5 oz chicken	Tomato Basil Soup 2 servings ½ avocado cubes on top
Snack 3:30 pm	Nut Butter and Brown Rice Cake 1.5 Tbsp Nut butter (almond, sunflower, etc) 1 Brown Rice Cake	Raw Walnut Fudge 2 servings	Nut Butter and Brown Rice Cake 1.5 Tbsp Nut butter (almond, sunflower, etc) 1 Brown Rice Cake	Raw Walnut Fudge 2 servings	Nut Butter and Brown Rice Cake 1.5 Tbsp Nut butter (almond, sunflower, etc) 1 Brown Rice Cake
Dinner 6:00-7 pm	Herby Tahini Salad with Grilled Shrimp Skewers 1.5 servings	Cauliflower Chowder 1.5 cups soup	Herby Tahini Salad with Grilled Shrimp Skewers 1.5 servings	Cauliflower Chowder 1.5 cups soup	Herby Tahini Salad with Grilled Shrimp Skewers 1.5 servings

Week 12
1200 calories

	Day 1	Day 2	Day 3	Day 4	Day 5
Breakfast 7:00 am	Superfood Smoothie 1 serving	Blueberry Flaxseed Overnight Oatmeal 1 serving	Superfood Smoothie 1 serving	Blueberry Flaxseed Overnight Oatmeal 1 serving	Superfood Smoothie 1 serving
Snack 10:00 am	Apple and Cashew Nut butter 1 apple + 1 Tbsp cashew nut butter	Cottage Cheese and Blueberries ¾ cup cottage cheese ½ cup blueberries	Apple and Cashew Nut butter 1 apple + 1 Tbsp cashew nut butter	Cottage Cheese and Blueberries ¾ cup cottage cheese ½ cup blueberries	Apple and Cashew Nut butter 1 apple + 1 Tbsp cashew nut butter
Lunch 12:30-1 pm	Minty Beet Almond Salad with Goat Cheese 1 serving	Pan Seared Chicken with Tomato Jam 1 serving	Colorful Soba Noodle Salad with Seared Buffalo 1 serving	Minty Beet Almond Salad with Goat Cheese 1 serving	Pan Seared Chicken with Tomato Jam 1 serving
Snack 3:30 pm	Peach and Macadamia Nuts 1 peach 5 macadamia nuts	Mango Chia Coconut Pudding 1 serving	Peach and Macadamia Nuts 1 peach 5 macadamia nuts	Mango Chia Coconut Pudding 1 serving	Peach and Macadamia Nuts 1 peach 5 macadamia nuts
Dinner 6:00-7 pm	Colorful Soba Noodle Salad with Seared Buffalo 1 serving	Minty Beet Almond Salad with Goat Cheese 1 serving	Pan Seared Chicken with Tomato Jam 1 serving	Colorful Soba Noodle Salad with Seared Buffalo 1 serving	Minty Beet Almond Salad with Goat Cheese 1 serving

Week 12
1800 calories

	Day 1	Day 2	Day 3	Day 4	Day 5
Breakfast **7:00 am**	Superfood Smoothie 1.5 servings	Blueberry Flaxseed Overnight Oatmeal 1.5 servings	Superfood Smoothie 1.5 servings	Blueberry Flaxseed Overnight Oatmeal 1.5 servings	Superfood Smoothie 1.5 servings
Snack **10:00 am**	Apple and Cashew Nut butter 1 apple + 2 Tbsp cashew nut butter	Cottage Cheese and Blueberries 1 cup cottage cheese 1 cup blueberries	Apple and Cashew Nut butter 1 apple + 2 Tbsp cashew nut butter	Cottage Cheese and Blueberries 1 cup cottage cheese 1 cup blueberries	Apple and Cashew Nut butter 1 apple + 2 Tbsp cashew nut butter
Lunch **12:30-1 pm**	Minty Beet Almond Salad with Goat Cheese 1.5 servings	Pan Seared Chicken with Tomato Jam 1.5 servings	Colorful Soba Noodle Salad with Seared Buffalo 1.5 servings	Minty Beet Almond Salad with Goat Cheese 1.5 servings	Pan Seared Chicken with Tomato Jam 1.5 servings
Snack **3:30 pm**	Peach and Macadamia Nuts 1 peach 10 macadamia nuts	Mango Chia Coconut Pudding 1 serving	Peach and Macadamia Nuts 1 peach 10 macadamia nuts	Mango Chia Coconut Pudding 1 serving	Peach and Macadamia Nuts 1 peach 10 macadamia nuts
Dinner **6:00-7 pm**	Colorful Soba Noodle Salad with Seared Buffalo 1.5 servings	Minty Beet Almond Salad with Goat Cheese 1.5 servings	Pan Seared Chicken with Tomato Jam 1.5 servings	Colorful Soba Noodle Salad with Seared Buffalo 1.5 servings	Minty Beet Almond Salad with Goat Cheese 1.5 servings

Terms & Resources

Glossary:

Chiffanade a knife technique where leafy greens or herbs are cut into tiny ribbons. Leaves are to be de-stemmed and stacked on top of one another, then they are rolled from the bottom to the top, and a knife is sliced through the roll of leaves perpendicular to the roll, creating tiny rings with each slice. The rings will unravel into tiny ribbons that are easy to manage. With large greens such as chard or kale, they may be sliced again once through the rings to reduce the length of the ribbons.

Sucanat unrefined cane sugar that retains molasses, b-vitamins, and minerals; also known as rapadura. This sweetener provides nutrients and is not refined so it will have irregular structure and crystallization size. If using one for one as a replacement for refined sugar, you may want to run through a blender or food processor to make smaller crystals that are easier to work with. As the flavor is more complex and rich, I suggest starting with ¾ to 1 replacement of sucanat for sugar.

Tamari wheat-free soy sauce that is traditionally fermented. Choose organic for a less toxic product. This can be replaced one for one with a soy sauce but note that soy sauce should also be organic or limit sodium benzoate; a toxic preservative found commonly in commercial soy sauce.
<u>Alternative to Tamari:</u> Braggs Liquid Aminos
<u>Soy-free alternatives to Tamari:</u> Coconut Aminos

Ghee clarified butter that has been separated with heat to remove casein, which is a common irritant found in dairy. This can be stored at room temperature as the casein is the element that risks rancidity. Select grass-fed organic for the most nourishing and lowest toxicity or make your own from grass-fed butter.

Matcha powdered form of a Japanese green tea that is grown in shade to increase certain properties and make the taste smooth with a less astringent after taste. Matcha is a ground powder of the entire leaf of tea, which is wholly consumed rather than steeping the leaf and discarding, which allows for about 10xs the nutritional boost. The use of shade in the growing process increases production of caffeine and L-Theonine a natural mood stabilizer.

Resources:

With all proteins, it is best to select a whole food with the least amount of parts removed. When selecting type within the specified cuts, choose bone-in, skin on to benefit from nutrients such as collagen, glutamine, and glycine while gaining the benefit of a juicier end-product with more complex flavor.

When selecting a protein source, consider the diet of the animal to determine the nutritional density and limit the toxicity. Choose sources that eat a traditional diet such as pasture-raised for poultry and pork, grass-fed for beef and dairy products, and wild-caught for fish and seafood. These options will be higher in omega-3 fatty acids, minerals, and antioxidants while ensuring the item is free of GMO-ingredients. Based on season and drought, some pasture-raised or grass-fed proteins will be provided supplemental feed to maintain optimal nutrition. This is acceptable but be sure to determine the source of grain and optimally avoid GMO-soy, GMO-corn, and GMO-alfalfa.

Resources to find clean proteins: www.eatwild.com and www.grasslandbeef.com. Also be sure to visit your local farmer's market and talk to your butcher. At Whole Foods, they have a numbering system of 1-4 where number 4 will be pasture-raised or grass-fed and 3 will be organic. Choose 4 whenever possible.

Poultry/Pork. Best options will be pasture-raised, hormone-free, antibiotic-free, bone-in, skin-on. Good options will be organic, and okay options will be hormone-free and antibiotic-free.

Beef. Best options will be grass-fed, hormone-free, antibiotic-free. Good options will be organic, and okay options will be hormone-free, antibiotic-free and non-GMO feed.

Fish. Best options will be wild-caught. Okay options will be sustainably farmed with non-GMO feed.

Eggs. Best options will be pasture-raised with non-GMO feed. Good options will be free-roaming, organic. Okay options are free-range, GMO-free.

Dairy. Choose grass-fed, full fat options that are organic for more vitamins, minerals, and CLA (conjugated linoleic acid) fatty acids that boost metabolism. This includes: grass-fed organic butter; non-homogenized low-heat pasteurized or raw milk in full fat form, and non-denatured grass-fed whey. When selecting yogurt, keifer, or other dairy products, choose sources free of sweeteners, stabilizers and fillers such as guar gum, carrageenan, and xanthan gum, which provide no nutritional value.

Lard. A saturated fat that is rich in fat-soluble nutrients and can tolerate high heat without oxidation or smoke point. Select lard from pasture-raised sources free of preservatives to limit toxicity or render your own. See recipe on our blog at: www.alimillerRD.com

Gelatin. Comprised of glycine and proline, two amino acids that are generally limited in the American diet but are found abundant in organs, bones, and fibrous animal tissues not commonly consumed. Choose grass-fed gelatin sources.

Collagen. The most abundant protein in the body, playing a role in the integrity of skin, tendons, muscle, and bone. This is a versatile product that can be used in smoothies, baked goods, and unlike gelatin it will not thicken in cold temperatures. Choose grass-fed sources.

Coconut milk choose canned options over cartons as they will be less watered down and select cans that are BPA-free to avoid toxins. Select full fat coconut milk that is made of only two ingredients: coconut and water. Avoid guar gum and carrageenan as these binders and fillers can be irritants to the gut and have pro-inflammatory effects.
Storage tip: Once the can is open consider storing in ice cube trays for convenient preservation and use in smoothies and recipes.

Almond Milk choose options that are free of carrageenan, guar gum, and other additives and stabilizers which can disrupt gut function and cause inflammation.
Make your own with 2 cups of soaked almonds blended with 5 cups of filtered water. Blend on high and strain with a cheese cloth or fine mesh of a "nut milk" bag.

Honey choose raw, unfiltered options to gain the most nutrition and local sources to gain the immune support for allergies to regional pollen.

Sea Salt is higher in minerals and lower in sodium than table salt. Sea salt will contain trace amounts of biological iodine vs. the synthetic form found in iodized salt. Other good salt alternatives are Himalayan pink salt, and grey salt.

Why Naturally Nourished Grass-fed Whey Protein?

Naturally Nourished Grass-fed Whey is a proprietary non-denatured native whey protein concentrate, produced to maintain the full range of all the fragile immune boosting and regenerative components naturally present in fresh raw milk.

Naturally Nourished Grassfed Whey protein is produced using proprietary filtration and drying which involves minimal processing. This unique production method ensures the whey is not subjected to temperatures that would destroy the original components. We do not use cross-flow filtration, microfiltration, hydrolyzation or ion exchange methods, which denature the original proteins.

This full range, biologically active, complete amino acid profile native protein naturally contains an exceptional amount of the critical glutathione precursor, covalent bonded cysteine. Glutathione is the most potent antioxidant, working to reduce heavy metal toxicity, reverse coronary artery calcification, aid in respiratory function, protect cellular health, and promote detoxification. Additionally, our unique grass-fed whey contains the full range of the most important immune supportive protein components, including lactoferrin, immunoglobins, IGG, serum albumin, and other beneficial growth factors supportive in treating leaky gut and autoimmune conditions.

The milk harvested for this product comes from cows that graze year-round on pesticide-free and chemical-free natural grass pastures. Milk from grass-fed cows has higher levels of conjugated lineoleic acids (CLA) and contains a proper balance of essential fatty acids; both of which have favorable outcomes on metabolism, lean body mass, brain health and cancer prevention. The milking cows are never fed grain or subjected to any growth hormones, chemicals, antibiotics, genetically modified organisms, hyperimmunization or injected pathogens.

To purchase Naturally Nourished Grass-Fed Whey Protein, go to www.AliMillerRD.com *and visit our Shop tab for all Naturally Nourished products. Also, check out our Amazon Store to find links for recommended brands of natural food products!*